_14_ Days

ANTARCTICA
Land of Frozen Time

by ROGER A. CARAS

Antarctica, a six-million-square-mile riddle locked in an ice age, sits on the bottom of planet Earth as the last great frontier for overland exploration. In his book, Roger Caras gives a total picture of the continent today, tomorrow, and yesterday, in words and pictures which will hold the reader spell-bound.

Its waters teem with more life than a tropical rain forest, and its coast plays host to the most magnificent animals in the world. Icebergs, as big as Connecticut, break loose from floating ice shelves larger than the whole of France to chill the ocean waters for thousands of miles.

Should the ice and snow of Antarctica melt, there would be no port city left in the world, and the Atlantic coastline of the United States would be in Pennsylvania. Are the snow and ice melting? Nobody knows for sure.

Antarctica now has nuclear power, yet life there is primitive. The continent has more scientists probing beneath its frozen surface than any other unknown area on this planet, yet her secrets and mysteries increase every day.

Revealed in majesty, the continent of mystery comes alive as never before. So, too, the stories of the men who pioneered the way to the far South—Shackleton, Scott, Amundsen, Byrd, and many more. Men have been drawn to the shores of this frozen world as if by a magnet—but their graves are often unmarked and their names unknown. Nobody knows how many have died; we only know their deaths were terrible.

This remarkable photograph of a Killer whale reaching up out of the Antarctic Ocean was taken by Morton Beebe, an equally remarkable photographer and a member of a team rapidly gaining fame under the name of "Globecombers." In Beebe's own words: "The circumstances surrounding the taking of the picture were: four of us were out late at night (2:00 A.M.) under the midnight sun seeking penguins and seals for a medical study. We were about five miles out on the thin (four to eight feet) McMurdo Bay ice chasing penguins when suddenly we were the subjects of a chase. Attracted by our movements, perhaps a dozen Killer whales took turns rising four feet, spiraling on their tails, out of the waters to view us above the ice level. They successfully began cracking the ice around us so as to tip us into the water. We then dashed back toward shore where the ice measured safely up to fourteen feet thick and the Killers departed."

ANTARCTICA: LAND OF FROZEN TIME

With Special Charts by A. Peter Ianuzzi

Illustrated

ANTARCTICA
LAND OF FROZEN TIME

Roger A. Caras

CHILTON BOOKS · A DIVISION OF CHILTON COMPANY
Publishers
Philadelphia and New York

Dedication

The pursuit of knowledge of, and in, far and unknown places is one of man's costliest enterprises. It takes not only his time, his energy, and his money, it also takes an inevitable toll in human life. In deep respect, this book is dedicated to the brave men who sleep forever in the eternal ice of the Antarctic—to those whose names are known and to those whose names are as lost to us as the whereabouts of their frozen graves.

A Note from the Author

One of the saddest things that can befall a person of adventurous mind, I believe, is the idea that the map is all filled in—that all the exploring has been done. To live in a world where all the great things have been accomplished would be to only half-live. It is the anticipation of adventure and the hope for personal accomplishment that best inspire people to prepare their bodies and their minds for the years that lie ahead.

Sometimes, sitting in an apartment in New York City watching television, or in a farmhouse in Kansas reading of the exploits of other people in other ages, it is hard to believe that man has only scratched the surface—that the map is still blank over millions upon millions of square miles. Happily for our generation and for generations yet unborn, this is so. We still have much to do on our own planet before turning *all* of our attention to outer space. Our world still needs explorers, still requires the services of brave men and women to understand its mysteries and harness its powers.

This book is about one of the largest blank areas on the map of planet Earth—the Antarctic.

Acknowledgments

It will be apparent to even the most casual reader that this book could not have been compiled and written without a great deal of help. Until an author tackles his first research subject in the non-fiction field, he has no idea of what his nuisance-potential is! I now know, and so do many of my friends. I am more than grateful to them all.

To Ivan Sanderson, thanks on a number of scores. By telling me to "stop talking and start writing," he proved the firm foundation of a friendship I cherish. For his constant guidance and occasional prodding, too, I am in his debt.

To Bob Rothenberg, with whom I fought over word-choice until the room temperature rose, my thanks for not agreeing. To Pete Ianuzzi, for his excellent charts and diagrams and for his expert guidance in matters scientific, I am more than grateful. There is no way to pay him for the hours he put in. To Phyllis and Jim Barclay, my gratitude for listening, and suggesting, and listening again. Thanks to Joan and Bob Perilla for being expert non-experts.

To Alice Sorensen, Janice Smith—the ladies of the typewriter—truly, my thanks; without them, quite simply, no book!

My special respects and thanks to Rear Admiral David M. Tyree, United States Navy, for playing host and accepting me as his guest in his Command-Antarctica. To Lieutenant Commander Jim Hahn and Chief Leo Loftus, my ever-lasting gratitude for their extraordinary hospitality in the Antarctic and at Christchurch, New Zealand. Their personal contributions to my education "on the ice" are beyond calculation. To the MATS and Navy air crews, ground crews, and general support personnel, for getting us there and back: my hat is off to you, gentlemen—I still don't know how you do it!

To the Department of the Navy, Office of Information, I am doubly indebted for arranging the trip and sticking with me when I got back. Special thanks to Commander Russ Bufkins for help far beyond measure.

The quotations from Scott's journals are reprinted by permission of Dodd, Mead & Company from *Scott's Last Expedition* by Robert Scott. Copyright 1913, 1941 by Dodd, Mead & Company, Inc.

My thanks to Mary H. Johnson of Stanford University Press for making the unique statistics from Victor Scheffer's *Seals, Sea Lions, and Walruses* available.

The statistical information on the construction of the hull of the *Endurance* is reprinted by permission of McGraw-Hill Book Company, Inc., from *Endurance: Shackleton's Incredible Voyage*, by Alfred Lansing. Copyright © 1959 by Alfred Lansing.

My thanks to the Department of State for clearance to reproduce the Antarctic Treaty and attending notes. My gratitude for the permission, granted by the Department of the Interior, to reproduce the list of expeditions compiled by Kenneth J. Bertrand and Fred G. Alberts for their *Geographic Names of Antarctica*.

Additional help was received from Remington Kellogg of the Smithsonian Institution, Walter W. Ristow of the Library of Congress, Mrs. Margaret Dodd of the Australian News and Information Bureau, Jon Embretsen of the Norwegian Embassy Information Service, Lieutenant (j.g.) Tom Coldwell, U.S.N., The British Information Services, Mr. D. Donaldson, Director-General of the New Zealand General Post Office, and a host of others. To all these ladies and gentlemen, my sincere thanks.

To wife Jill, daughter Pamela, and son Clay, my humblest thanks for your understanding and cooperation. I now resume my duties as husband and father, with a big debt to pay.

ROGER A. CARAS

Kew Gardens, N. Y.

Contents

ANTARCTICA: LAND OF FROZEN TIME

1

What Is the Antarctic?

THERE are many ways to describe what we call Antarctica or The Antarctic, and most of the things we can say about it sound unreal. This is so because almost everything we can say about it will be foreign to all of your own experiences, different from anything you can have known in your own world. Imagine it this way—it is colder than you thought it could be (the air temperature approaches the temperature of dry ice!), it is windier than Florida's worst hurricane, and it carries snow and ice over most of its nearly 6,000,000 square miles, deeper than anywhere else on Earth. When you stand at the South Pole itself, you are standing on snow and ice 2 miles deep!

The Antarctic is the coldest, windiest, and highest continent on this planet Earth. It is the fifth largest continent, and the average altitude is close to 7,000 feet. Most of it is almost totally unexplored.

Picture a land larger than the United States and Mexico combined that towers, on the average, well over a mile into the sky. Think of a land where plant life is almost completely unknown today, although it was once covered with forests, before the ice advanced. Aside from a few reptilian fossils, tentatively reported as resembling those of the Permian period of South Africa, little is known of extinct life. However, many mysteries lie locked in the ice, awaiting

1

The Ross Ice Shelf—first view of Antarctica for most American visitors today.

discovery. Imagine a land that only 60 years ago was not universally accepted as even existing, except as a chain of frozen islands. Think of all this and then let your imagination run wild, and you will probably come up with something that resembles the subject matter of this book.

Once known as Terra Australus Incognita—Unknown Land of the South—the Antarctic is just now becoming known; our understanding of it is just beginning. *You* are in on the ground floor of one of man's great adventures.

Antarctica is, as has been said, the fifth largest continent. It is almost twice the size of Australia and over 50 times the size of New Zealand. You could lose England in a corner of it, and it might take you years to find it again. France could sit on one of the many floating ice shelves that are fed by its glaciers and hold much of its shoreline aloof from any ship man yet knows how to produce.

As a land mass, Antarctica is surrounded by water—the Antarctic Ocean. This ocean starts at 66½° South and runs completely around the world. North of that 66½° line this ocean becomes the Atlantic, the Pacific, and the Indian Oceans. The Antarctic Ocean is dramatically affected by the frozen continent and, in turn, affects all the other interconnecting oceans of the world. Billions of tons of ice float free from Antarctica each year and carry some of the eternal chill northward toward warmer climes. The bitter-cold coastline creates cold ocean currents that affect much of the world. Great hurricanes of frosty air scream down from the high plateau along the routes followed by the flowing rivers of plastic ice and roar out over the roughest seas in the world. Antarctica is a restless and monstrous refrigeration plant.

The Antarctic is a land full of dramatic realities that will, one day, have a great deal to do with the life of man on Earth. We are already very much affected by these factors, about which subject we shall have more to say later. However, there are some other things that might be of interest to you before we begin our journey back into the Ice Age.

If you loaded 5,000 tons of cargo onto a ship at the Equator, and managed to land that cargo on the Antarctic coast and transport it over the ice, up onto the plateau (no easy task!), it would weigh 25 tons more by the time you got it to the South Pole than when you started. This strange fact is due to the spinning motion of our planet: the centrifugal force resulting from this motion makes things heavier at the Pole than at the Equator or anywhere in between.

It is now believed that between 90 and 95 per cent of all the ice in the world lies on the frozen back of the Antarctic. That means that all the ice and snow in Greenland, Switzerland, Canada, Siberia, in the area of the North Pole, and all the snow that falls on Maine, North Dakota, Wyoming, and all the rest of the world amounts to less than 10 per cent of the total. The Antarctic has, at the very least, nine times as much snow and ice as the rest of the world lumped together. The water locked up in the glaciers of the Antarctic is greater in quantity than that contained in all the rivers and lakes of the world.

The important thing to know about all this ice and snow is not so much just its quantity but, rather, what it can mean to the people of the world. If that snow and ice ever melt, the oceans of the world will rise 200 feet, drown every coastline, and wipe out every port, harbor, bay, and coastal city on Earth. The only tourist who would be able to visit the Statue of Liberty would be an adventurous skin-diver with a boat good enough to carry him across the sea from central Pennsylvania, where the Atlantic coastline would lie.

3

The obvious question to ask is, "Will the snow and the ice ever melt?" No one knows the answer for sure, but we have some clues. The Antarctic was not always covered with ice. It was once rich in plant life and thick forests—we have found fossils to prove it beyond a shadow of a doubt. Also, it is believed that the Antarctic today gives a pretty fair picture of what much of North America must have looked like when the great glaciers crept down from the North. Most of North America shed those glaciers to become what it is today. Glaciers and ice ages do retreat—the Antarctic was ice-free in the past. Who is to say that this won't happen again? How do we know it isn't happening now? Indeed, many scientists have found good reason to think that it is.

To most people, the words "South Pole" are synonymous with Antarctica; but this, of course, is not the case. The South Pole is one point (or rather five points, as we shall see) on the huge icy continent. The South Pole is, perhaps, the most confusing place on our planet (except for the North Pole), and for many reasons. Not the least astounding thing about it is that it is five things, depending on what you mean when you talk about it.

The **Geographic South Pole** is the southernmost point on the Earth's surface. It is here that the 360 degrees of longitude come together. Since longtitude is a measure of time, and not just of distance, the day's 24 hours all converge here as well. There is really no "time" at the Pole. No matter what your watch says, even if it has stopped, it is correct! Because the International Date Line terminates here, you can move from Saturday to Sunday or vice versa by taking one step. Actually, there is only one day and one night per year. In September, the sun comes up and slowly spirals around the sky. Noon arrives after 3 months of this spiraling. In March, the sun sets, and there are 6 months of darkness. If you walk around the Pole, you walk completely around the world in those few steps. If you were to take 24 steps to go around the Pole, you should change your watch one hour at each step, backward or forward, depending on the direction you chose to walk. And, of course, there is only one direction at the bottom—North. This is one of the two places on Earth from whence it is impossible to go toward either the East or the West.

The **Geomagnetic South Pole** is the point where the lines of the earth's magnetic field converge. This point is about 790 miles from the Geographic South Pole.

The **Magnetic South Pole** is the spot at which the compass needle on a magnetic compass points straight down. This is, perhaps, the

The Wilson-Piedmont Glacier, Victoria Land and a Navy helicopter on a scientific mission.

most confusing Pole of all, since it is constantly on the move. It is frequently as far as between 1,000 and 2,000 miles from the Geographic South Pole.

The **Pole of Inaccessibility** is that point on the Antarctic continent which is farthest inland from all shorelines. It is situated approximately 550 miles from the Geographic South Pole. Presumably, it is the most difficult place to reach in Antarctica.

The **Spin Pole** is an imaginary point at which the Earth's axis sticks out. Since the Earth wobbles as it spins on its axis, the Spin Pole has a wavering path. The Spin Pole is at the same spot on Earth as the Geographic South Pole.

Actually, all of the poles are imaginary, insofar as a visible position goes. They exist only as a result of our ability to measure the world in which we live and the great dynamic forces that shape and control it. If you didn't have instruments to make the complex measurements, you could walk over the five Poles and never know the difference. The sensation at each of them would be the same—cold! It is important, however, to understand what we mean when we talk about the Pole. Unless it is clearly stated otherwise, when we talk about the Pole in this book we will be talking about the Geographic South Pole.

The coldest temperature ever recorded on the surface of the Earth, not counting those artificially produced in laboratories, was noted in August of 1960 at Russia's Vostok Base, in the interior of the Antarctic continent—approximately 126° below zero, Fahrenheit. In September of 1959, the temperature recorded by American scientists at the South Pole was 110° below zero. When this author visited the South Pole in November of 1961, springtime in the Antarctic, the temperature was still down −47° below zero. Spring, to the rest of the world, means sunshine, budding trees, and the first flowering plants. At the bottom of the world, a spring day with the temperature at its highest point is still far colder than almost anywhere else on Earth.

The extremes of wind velocity are as spectacular and as dangerous as those of temperature. Commonwealth Bay in the Antarctic is believed to be the windiest region in the world. During one July, when careful records were kept, the mean velocity was over 55 miles per hour. During one day in August, 1913, an average velocity of over 80 miles an hour was recorded. Winds of 200 miles an hour have been experienced more than once. Compare this with the great hurricanes that spread terror throughout the southeastern United States: they seldom attain speeds as high as 135 miles per hour!

Besides being colder and windier than the Arctic, the Antarctic is different in other ways from the region of the North Pole. The Antarctic, as we have seen, is a great body of land surrounded by water. The Arctic is a great body of water surrounded by land. This water accounts for the warmer temperatures in the North. The South Pole rests on an ice plateau about 10,000 feet high. If the North Pole were actually a marker of some kind, instead of just a location on a map, you would find it at the bottom of a frigid sea, 10,000 feet down. That seems to be enough of a difference—20,000 feet! Now let's explore this land at the bottom of planet Earth.

2

Man Seeks the Bottom of His World:
From the Beginning to 1899

I T is a wise explorer who begins his expedition in a
good library. Exploration is not the sudden inspired
deed of one man but a slender thread that has been unraveling
through all of human history. We learn from both the successes and
the failures of those who have gone before, and where we stop others
will begin. Since we are explorers in a very real sense, let's take a
look at the record of man south of 66° South.

We may never know where and when Antarctic exploration really
began. Evidence is scanty and confusing; and there are several
legendary voyages, reports of which have filtered down through the
centuries. These exist only as tales without any real supporting evidence. There is as much nonsense about the history of the world
south of 66° South as north of it. Let us look for facts, where we can
discern them.

Amerigo Vespucci, after whom America is named, is supposed
to have reached South Georgia, an island in the extreme South
Atlantic, as far back as 1502. It is doubtful that he really did—there
are no real facts to support such a claim, and it was not quite the
type of voyage he was equipped to make.

In the year 1603, Spanish privateers captured the Dutch ship
Blyde Bootschap. On board the pirates' prize was an observant young

boatswain, Laurens Claess, who evidently had a better-than-average education, judging from his reports of the events that followed his captain's surrender. He tells of sighting a large and miserably bleak island at 64° South when the captive ship was driven off course by a vicious gale. If we have analyzed his observation properly, he *may have been* the first man to sight *and* record the existence of the South Shetland Islands, near the Antarctic Circle. That's probably about as far south as the Jolly Roger ever flew!

There is substantial evidence that an English merchant, Antonio de la Roche, with two ships whose names are lost to us, discovered South Georgia and took shelter there while running before a furious South Atlantic storm in 1675. South Georgia is about 54° South, still 12½° North of the Antarctic Circle. If Antonio did, in fact, hide from that storm on South Georgia, he may not have reached the Antarctic, but he got pretty close. It is more likely that he, and not Vespucci, discovered the island.

We are reasonably certain that a number of other sailing ships sighted Antarctic Islands well back in time; but since these visits were, to all intents and purposes, accidental, we can't really call them voyages of exploration. We know that the Spanish merchantman *Leon* sighted and circumnavigated South Georgia in 1756, for a passenger on that ship, Dveloz Guyot, wrote an account of the incident which has survived. He doesn't seem to have been very impressed by what he saw, but we must be grateful to him for recording the event.

Just about as far south as South Georgia lies a craggy mass of rock and ice known as Bouvet Island or Bouvetoya. It is only about 5 miles long, and terminates in steep rock and ice cliffs all around its storm-wracked perimeter. Its waters are almost always fogged over and clogged with floating ice. It is a most inhospitable place. On New Year's Day, 1739, this cold and lonely land was discovered, probably for the first time, by J. B. C. Bouvet de Lozier. This French explorer was using two ships, the *Aigle* and the *Marie*, but neither vessel dared penetrate the combination of fog and ice, and no landing was attempted. Bouvet de Lozier was a wise man, for floating ice masses would have smashed the wooden hulls of his ships as if they were made of paper. His were not proper polar ships.

Bouvet Island was resighted in 1808 and identified as an island by the British ships *Snow Swan* and *Otter;* but it was not until the German ship *Valdivia* visited the island, 90 years later, that the insular nature and the position of the lonely outpost were determined. Today, Bouvet Island belongs to Norway.

8

The U.S. flag at the Geographic South Pole.

Bouvet Island is not an important feature on the surface of our planet. It may never be explored thoroughly, and man may never require it for any practical purpose, except perhaps to house an automatic weather station. We have discussed its history in some detail here only because it seems to be rather typical of Antarctic land masses. There were at least four countries involved in its being put on our maps—France, England, Germany, and Norway. We don't know for certain who first saw it or landed on it, but the first three visits of which we have information span a period of 159 years, from 1739 to 1898. There is a good chance that any really modern survey that might be attempted will uncover surprising errors in the estimates of its size and position. Recent surveys in the Antarctic have found mountains misplaced on the map by as much as 60 miles; and some recorded features, including islands, were found not to exist at all!

Most of the surface of our planet is under water. Each year, with the explosive growth of our population and increasing human needs, any land breaking through the surface of our seas gains added significance. Unfortunately, there are many "Bouvet Islands" in the world—land that is bleak and barren, inaccessible, and incapable of supporting human life by any means now reasonably at our disposal. As we shall see, the Antarctic has more than its share of seemingly useless "dry land." The time is already in the foreseeable future, when man will hardly be able to afford the waste of any 20 square miles of land. The "Bouvet Islands" on our planet may, one day, be major causes for concern and, collectively, an essential focus for our attention.

Before going on, in this and the next chapter, to recount the major exploits of Antarctic exploration, we should acknowledge the greatest single mystery in all of Antarctic lore—the "Piri Reis, Columbus map of 1513"!

If we do a little research, we will find that a man named Piri Reis helped conquer the coasts of Yemen and Aden, as far as the Gulf of Basra, during Turkey's period of empire-building. He compiled a detailed atlas of the Aegean and the Mediterranean, conquered Muscat, and helped lay siege to the city of Ormuz. Eventually, he was executed on the ground that he had sold out to the Portuguese enemy. With all due respect to the jurisprudence of the time, we shall never know whether Admiral Piri Reis really was a traitor. We probably shall never know very much about him at all. We have been *told* that, some time during his stormy career, he captured a ship, or took a port city, and found himself the captor of a man who is *said* to have been Christopher Columbus' pilot. From this prisoner he is supposed to have obtained a "Portolano Chart," one of the maps used by Columbus on his first voyage in 1492.

Piri Reis evidently made a hobby of collecting charts, because he combined this priceless souvenir with others, some dating as far back as three centuries before Christ. He drew his famous map in 1513, incorporating data all the way back to the time of Alexander the Great and before. Drawn on gazelle skin and beautifully hand-colored, the map still exists in Istanbul, Turkey.

This strange relic of the mathematical and geographical genius of an all-but-forgotten Turkish admiral has confounded cartographers for years. There is much about it that is obscure and obviously quite fanciful. Yet, there is much about it that demands attention and serious study. We are interested in it here because, if one interpretation of it is correct, it shows a ship-studded, ice-free coastline of Antarctica—as it is supposed to have been 5,000 years ago!! It seems impossible, but there it is. Further research could prove this to be true—the great land of ice, as recently as 5,000 years ago, in part at least, free of ice and visited by man. This would be in direct conflict with almost everything we know, or think we know, about the bottom of our planet. We can neither prove nor disprove this theory—not yet, at any rate. We can predict that there will be a lot of arguments, and perhaps even a little name-calling, before this problem is resolved. This author takes *no* stand on the subject.

There is another strange incident that may, one day, figure in the investigation of this matter. In 1893, a Norwegian sealer named Captain C. A. Larsen found 50 clay balls perched on small pillars of the same material. The find was made on Seymour Island, off the eastern coast of the Palmer Peninsula, farther south than that of any other known primitive artifacts. He reported that "these had the appearance of having been made by human hands." No one yet has found grounds for doubting the Captain's word, nor has anyone satisfactorily explained his discovery. (Not all the answers, by any means, are in about the history of the Antarctic.) Captain Larsen's clay relics and Piri Reis' map are still in the realm of the unexplained. Let us return to facts we can explain and history we can interpret. In doing so, it should be noted, we are returning from the twilight zone of man's knowledge, the borderline between fact and fancy, history and intellectual histrionics. What wonders we may one day uncover in this zone, when our eyes become sharp enough to penetrate the mist!

The most important known voyage of discovery in Antarctic waters prior to 1800 was made by the great Captain James Cook. His ships were the *Resolution* and the *Adventure*, both suitably named, to be sure.

By the year 1770, events in history had progressed to the point where the great unsolved mystery of the legendary Southern Continent had to be resolved. France and England had nearly gone to war over the Falkland Islands, not far north of the Antarctic region in the Atlantic Ocean. Cook had distinguished himself greatly in his first voyage, and had the personal attention of the King of

Captain James Cook

England and private investors. Man's inquisitive mind had burst loose, and any mystery as great and commanding as an unknown continent nagged at his very soul. Man had to know! Collectively, he was uneasy about having anything as great as an entire continent, reports of which had been drifting into view out of the fog of unrecorded history for hundreds of years, escape his attention. An island here and there, yes, but a whole continent—never!

Man had sailed far to the north—he had sailed around the world, he had discovered strange peoples, plants, and animals. Each new find brought him new treasures, new flavors, new wealth, and fre-

12

quently, although he wasn't always aware of them, new diseases. Perhaps, if he could sail far to the south, even greater spoils would be his. We must remember that it was not known at the time whether or not land existed at the bottom, nor what that land would be like if it did exist. Some insisted it would be tropical!

Toward the end of 1771, the British Admiralty purchased two solid Whitby colliers for Cook's use. Originally designed to transport coal, these colliers were particularly stout little vessels. They were much like the *Endeavour* used by him on his first voyage, and were considered especially strong and safe. At first, they were named *Drake* and *Raleigh;* but later, their names were changed to *Resolution* and *Adventure,* lest the Spaniards feel resentful that two Elizabethan seadogs be so remembered and honored.

On February 6, 1772, Captain Cook submitted his proposed itinerary to Lord Sandwich, First Lord of the Admiralty. It began: ". . . Upon due consideration of the discoveries that have been made in the Southern Ocean, and the tracks of the ships which have made these discoveries, it appears that no Southern lands of great extent can extend to the Northward of 40 degrees latitude, except about the meridian of 140° West, every other part of the Southern Ocean have at different times been explored . . . Therefore to make new discoveries the Navigator must Traverse or Circumnavigate the Globe in a higher parallel than has hitherto been done . . . The principal thing to be attended to is the proper Season of Year, for Winter is by no means favourable for discoveries in these Latitudes, . . ." The rest of the memorandum outlined his plans for stopovers and winter activities. As it turned out, he stayed very close to his plans.

The sloop *Resolution* was "burdthen 462 Tons to be man'd with 110 Men including officers and to carry twelve guns." The sloop *Adventure,* commanded by Captain Tobias Turneaux, was "Burdthen 336 tons, 80 men, and ten guns." It is interesting to note some of the supplies Captain Cook laid in, remembering that it was this great explorer who was one of the first to realize the true cause of scurvy, a disease that heretofore had decimated crews on extended voyages. Despite the complaints of his men and the scorn of his peers, he insisted that vegetables were the preventive and the cure. Among other things, he loaded onto the *Resolution* 19,337 pounds of "Sour Kraut," 400 pounds of mustard, 19 half-barrels of "Inspisated Juce of Beer," 642 gallons of wine, and "210 Gallons Oyle Olive." Beef, pork, cereals, raisins, suet, malt, cabbage, biscuit, butter, cheese, and a dozen other items complete the list.

Cook sailed from Plymouth in July of 1772 and made for Cape Town. He arrived at Africa's southern tip three and a half months later. At Cape Town, Cook learned of French expeditions working in southern latitudes, and sailed for the south-west. Skipping down through his log we find comments about the weather he encountered:

Saturday, 12th December—52°56′ South—"Fresh gales and Hazy Foggy weather with sleet and snow"; *Monday, 14th December— 54°55′ South*—"at half past six we were stopped by an immence field of ice to which we could see no end . . . where we saw many Penguins and Whales . . ."; *Friday, 18th December—54°57′ South* —"the gale Freshened and brought with it snow and sleet which freezed on our Rigging and Sails as it fell . . . carried us a mong the Islands which we had enough to do to keep clear of. Of two evils I thought this the least. Dangerous as it is sailing a mongest the floating Rocks in a thick Fog and unknown sea yet it is preferable to being intangled with Field Ice under the same circumstances."

We can assume the "floating Rocks" to be icebergs and the "Field Ice" to be what we today call "pack ice." Cook was right, as we shall see, for this pack ice is a treacherous foe and subsequently proved to be the Nemesis of many a brave Antarctic sailor.

What Cook finally accomplished was a circumnavigation of the globe south of 50° South. He penetrated the Antarctic Circle three times, roughly charted the north coast of South Georgia, and made the first known landing there. He discovered part of the South Sandwich Islands, and roughly charted them. Cook's voyage finally disproved the existence, so long accepted, of an unknown southern continent north of the Antarctic Circle, and laid the foundation for future exploration. It is believed that he reached the southernmost point of his life on January 30, 1774—71°10′ South. Cook, usually a modest man, was bold enough to declare that he had sailed as far south as it was possible to go, and that no man would go farther. The great explorer, certainly one of the greatest who ever lived, was, in time, proved to be wrong.

Between 1800 and 1900, we know of 56 recorded expeditions and have reason to believe there were others. Of these 56 expeditions, 36 were sealing or whaling ventures; and exploration was usually either accidental, or, at least, secondary to commercial interests. Since officers and men shared in the profits of these trips, and since the season was short, attention was paid to the problem of capturing seals and whales. Few skippers were far-sighted enough

14

to know, or at least care, that exploration of this unknown region would one day have meanings far greater than could be measured in terms of dollars and cents. A few did care, and later expeditions owed much to their skill as navigators and observers. It must be remembered, too, that if exploration uncovered new sealing or whaling grounds, the valuable secret was jealously guarded.

During the 19th century, 19 of the 56 expeditions were American in origin, 24 were British, 1 Russian, 1 Belgian, 1 Scottish, and 4 German. France and Australia each sent 1, as did Argentina; and Norway sent 3. Before we get carried away about American and British exploration in the far South during the 1800's, we should recognize that most of this activity was inspired by the dollars and pounds to be found in whale oil and sealskins, and not by undiscovered land. Whatever exploring was done by these commercial expeditions was generally inspired by the lure of new whaling and sealing grounds, and not by science. We can't be too critical of that, however, because it is only very recently that pure science became a recognizable motive for exploration on a large scale, always a very expensive proposition. After all, Columbus discovered the Western Hemisphere, as the story goes, in the search for India and the spice trade. I don't think good Queen Isabella would have sold her now famous, but almost certainly fictional, jewels to humor the academic fancies of some crackpot from Genoa. The Admiral of the Ocean Seas talked good sense—dollars and cents—and got his ships. The world gained a new hemisphere quite by accident, so we are told. Perhaps it wasn't really the first time Europe learned of the New World, but it was the first time with good publicity!

There are a number of interesting highlights to Antarctic exploration during the 19th century, despite the paucity of interest in pure science. In the years 1819–1821, Captain Thaddeus Bellingshausen, a German in the employ of Czar Alexander I and the Russian Navy, explored Antarctic waters by circumnavigating the world, mostly south of the Circle. Although his two ships, the *Vostok* and the *Mirny*, sighted many islands, there is no evidence to support the argument that he raised the main Antarctic land mass. Today, the Bellingshausen Sea honors his name; and two Russian bases, built during the IGY (International Geophysical Year) and still in operation, commemorate his stout and sturdy sailing ships— Mirny on the west coast and Vostok, the coldest known place on Earth, on the polar plateau. In the final analysis, up to that time his expedition was second in importance only to Captain Cook's.

15

In 1820–1821, a U.S. sealing expedition under Captain Benjamin Pendleton operated in the South Atlantic with five ships. One of these ships, the *Hero*, was under the command of Captain Nathaniel B. Palmer, not yet 21 years old. There is good reason to believe that, in January of 1821, Palmer explored the great, bleak peninsula which reaches up from the mainland toward South America and now bears his name. He *may* have sighted the mainland earlier, on November 17, 1820. Palmer and the men of the *Hero* were probably the first to sight the Antarctic continent. During these same two years, another American sealing expedition landed what we must assume to be the first men ashore on the mainland.

It was around 10:00 A.M. on February 7, 1821, that a heavy, open whale boat picked its way through floating pancakes of ice to Hughes Bay on the Antarctic continent and the men scrambled ashore. We don't know exactly why these men were put ashore in this desolate region, but, perhaps, it was to examine the sealing potential of the new area. Captain John Davis watched from the deck of his ship, *Cecilia*, and later wrote: "I think this Southern Land to be a continent." Perhaps if Captain Davis had known that this was to be the first time that known men would walk on the fifth largest continent on our planet, he would have joined his crew. To the best of available knowledge, it *was* the first landing ever made on the mainland.

The years 1820–1822 were particularly busy ones south of 66° South. We know of 25 expeditions active in those two years, nearly half of all the known expeditions of the whole century.

This period of exploration was not without its tragedies. On December 9, 1820, the American sealer *Clothier* was wrecked in what is now Clothier Harbor in the South Shetlands Islands. On December 25 of the same year, the British vessel *Lady Trowbridge* went down off King George Island. On December 28, the *Cecilia*, just a few months before she landed her party at Hughes Bay, rescued a British crew who had been stranded when their ship went down. The captain of the *Lady Trowbridge*, Richard Sherrat, survived the disaster, and his records and observations have come down to us. We can reasonably speculate that it was the crew of the *Lady Trowbridge* the *Cecilia* rescued. Perhaps members of the rescued British crew were in the Hughes Bay landing party, making this probable first an international affair. Between 1833–1834, the British ship *Hopeful* was crushed by ice west of the South Shetlands.

We shall never know how many ships went down nor how many

men died, during those early years, in Antarctic waters. Except in cases where violent storms capsized vessels, making a sudden end for the crew, we can assume that floating ice caused slower and more painful deaths for the ships and the men. We can imagine great sailing ships with their sides stove in and crews working desperately for hours and, perhaps, days on end at the hand pumps. Temperatures are far below freezing. There is neither heat nor hot food aboard the stricken ship. Men fall exhausted to the deck, as the sea begins to act up, undoing in minutes the pitiful progress they have made in hours of back-breaking labor. The captain finally concedes that it is hopeless, and the surviving men scramble over the sides into open boats or onto floating ice. They carry what little food, clothing, and shelter they can, and watch the ice hammer and crush their ship out of existence, from an ironically safe distance. The captain, in optimism, has saved his charts and navigational instruments.

We wonder how many of these lonely, frozen men slowly died from exposure in their open boats, on thin ice rafts, and on the shores of lifeless, rocky islets they may have reached before finally perishing. What stories of bravery could be told, and perhaps stories of horror, telling of men, half mad, turning to cannibalism. The Antarctic is the perfect villainess—the horrors of her deeds are forever secret.

It was during the 1838–1842 U.S. Exploring Expedition under Lieutenant Charles Wilkes, U.S.N., that the Antarctic land mass was proved to be of continental proportions. It was another 60 years or so before this was universally accepted, but we can trace our knowledge of that fact to those dates.

When we look at the map of Antarctica today, we are reminded at every turn of the men who faced the hazards and of the ships that carried them there. The map is a chart of tribute: Bouvet de Lozier, Captain James Cook, Nathaniel Palmer, Thaddeus Bellingshausen, the *Vostok* and the *Mirny*, Captain James Weddell, the *Clothier*, Captain John Biscoe, Captain Dumont D'Urville, Lieutenant Charles Wilkes, Captain James Clark Ross, the *Erebus* and the *Terror*, Lieutenant Adrien de Gelache, and dozens more recall the stories of past exploits. It is not enough, however, that a volcano, a bay, a segment of ice-covered plateau, or a frigid spit of land be named after a man. These men of the 19th century gave us more than names for geographical features. They created a heritage, and gave us facts and techniques, that one day would meld into a firm foundation for Antarctic travel and exploration. The day will come when man will use the Antarctic just as he will the ocean abyss and the surface of the moon. He will owe his ability to do so as much to the brave and strong of the 19th century as he will to the enlightened and the well-equipped of the 20th. This is not to be construed as a slight to the men of recent and contemporary times. As we shall see, bravery and fortitude did not fade away as the 20th century dawned.

3

Man Finds the Bottom of His World:
From 1900 to the Present

THE years 1900 to 1910 saw 19 expeditions set sail for the Antarctic. In just 10 years, a number equalling one third of all of the known expeditions of the previous 100 years marked the beginning of the end of Antarctica's solitary confinement. Man had come to stay below 66° South.

Great Britain, Germany, Sweden, Scotland, Argentina, France, Norway—all participated in Antarctic exploration during the first decade of our century. There is no record of an American expedition during those years. Of all that happened during that brief period, we are most aware today that three men appeared on the scene. Each in his own way was, one day, to make his mark on the history of the Land of the South. The exploits of each stand high on the list of human accomplishments. No story of the Antarctic can be complete without recording the feats of Robert Falcon Scott, Ernest Henry Shackleton, and Roald Engebreght Gravning Amundsen.

In 1899, a 31-year-old lieutenant in the British Navy was recommended by his superiors to command the British National Antarctic Expedition then being formed. In making this recommendation, they were condemning the young officer to death, and to ever-lasting fame and glory, for the name Robert Falcon Scott has come to be the very symbol of Antarctic exploration. From the time of the rec-

19

Captain Robert Falcon Scott

ommendation till the time of his death, Scott had 13 years of life. During that brief span of years, he developed a love affair with the Antarctic such as few men have known. It became an obsession with him and lasted until he was entombed by it.

In 1900, the Admiralty acted on the recommendation it had received and, promoting Scott to the rank of Commander, gave him the expedition. On his ship *Discovery*, Scott encountered the first pack ice of his life on January 1, 1902. In the Antarctic, he proved to be an intrepid and able leader as well as a highly competent scientific investigator. He was rewarded with the rank of Captain upon his return to England in 1904.

Hut Point, where Scott and his party set up their headquarters, is a pile of volcanic rubble that juts out from frigid Ross Island into McMurdo Sound. It is within easy walking distance of the U.S.N.'s Deep Freeze headquarters, and this author walked out to it in November of 1961. The hut, now packed solid with drift snow, is impossible to enter. Scattered about are cases of dog biscuits, a half-consumed mutton carcass, and other debris of early expeditions. Nearby is a cross erected by Scott's men to honor the memory of a sailor, George Vince, who lost his footing and plunged to his death over a cliff, now known as Danger Slopes.

Scott and his men used the hut as a storage facility and spent the winter of 1902 aboard the 700-ton *Discovery*, frozen solid in the ice just 200 yards off shore. Later expeditions were to make more use of the historic hut than Scott himself.

Hut Point is a bleak and barren place. The scattered remnants of early expeditions, the lonely cross, the ever-smoking volcano Mt. Erebus sending an endless spiral of gas up into the streams of frigid wind blowing across from the mainland, are the impressions one gets. It is hard to understand with what it was that Scott fell in love. Perhaps it was with destiny more than with the landscape.

Scott's first expedition was a success. His geographic exploration and scientific observations added considerably to the limited knowledge then available. Several long sledge journeys were made, including one on the Ross Ice Shelf over 380 miles long. On one of these journeys, Scott's young lieutenant, Ernest Shackleton, fell ill and had to be hauled out on a sledge by his companions. Shackleton's later exploits, as we shall see, more than made up for this somewhat inglorious end to his first Antarctic venture.

Scott's first hut as it looks today.

Official U.S. Navy Photograph

90°S

14 December 1911
R.AMUNDSEN
O.BJAALAND
H.HANSSEN
S.HASSEL
O.WISTING

18 January 1912
R.F.SCOTT
E.A.WILSON
H.R.BOWERS
L.E.G.OATES
E.EVANS

A tribute from Great Britain and Norway 1961
...ted to the U.S. Amundsen-Scott South Pole Station

Official U.S. Navy Photograph

The Amundsen-Scott plaque now at the South Pole station.

Between 1904 and 1909, Scott performed his normal duties as a British naval officer. In the back of his mind, however, there burned but a single thought—one ambition—get back to the ice! In 1909, he announced his intentions and set about gaining support. His declared plan was for him to be the first human being to reach the South Pole.

The frustrations and obstacles he encountered in preparing for the assault on the very bottom of the world were nearly overwhelming. Suffice it to say that the *Terra Nova* sailed from England in 1910 and reached Ross Island on January 3, 1911—9 years and 2 days after Scott crossed the Antarctic Circle for the first time. Although subsidiary scientific field work was carried out by his party, Scott's main purpose and personal obsession were to reach the Pole. He was driven on by the news that an experienced and seasoned Arctic explorer from Norway, Roald Amundsen, was out for the same goal. Amundsen had made up an expedition to be first at the North Pole, but when he learned that Admiral Peary had beaten him there, he decided to try for its opposite in the South.

Scott planned on using Siberian ponies and tractors, while Amundsen relied on dogs to pull his sledges. This was one of several factors that was to give the Norwegian glory and life and the Englishman bitter disappointment and death. Before Amundsen ever dreamed of going for the South Pole himself, he and Scott met and discussed the latter's plans. Amundsen advised him against using ponies, stating that dogs alone could fulfill the needs of the mission. Despite Scott's admiration for the Norwegian, he didn't take his advice.

The U.S. Navy's scientific installation at the South Pole is known as Amundsen-Scott Base, and a plaque presented to the United States by the British and the Norwegian governments adorns the

Norwegian Information Service

Amundsen's ship, the FRAM.

Roald Amundsen

wall of the mess hall, deep under the snow and ice. On it are the names of the men who made up the two parties: Scott, Evans, Oates, Wilson, and Bowers—Amundsen, Bjaaland, Hanssen, Hassel, and Wisting. The story of the race between Scott and Amundsen to be first at the Pole is *the* classic tale of Antarctic exploration. The Norwegians won by reaching the Pole on December 14, 1911, more than a month ahead of the Englishmen, who finally made it on January 17, 1912.

Two factors, perhaps more than any others, gave victory to Amundsen. He was fortunate enough to choose an easier route up onto the Polar plateau from the eastern end of the Ross Ice

Shelf, while Scott worked up the incredibly difficult Beardmore Glacier from the west.

The second determining factor seems to have been the choice of sledge animals. Amundsen's dogs survived the trip while Scott's snow ponies gave out early on the inbound trip, forcing the Englishmen to man-haul their loads for close to 1500 miles. (The tractors proved to be altogether useless.) It is almost impossible to understand how this was accomplished. In many places the plateau is two miles high, and the rarefied air makes breathing terribly difficult, even without physical exertion. How it was within the bounds of human capability for five men to fight their way up the 155-mile slope of the tortuous Beardmore Glacier, and man-haul tons of supplies across that frozen, wind-swept plateau, is beyond understanding. When this author arrived at the South Pole in 1961, in safety and comfort aboard a Navy C-130 Hercules, his first comment was, "How did they do it? How was it possible?" In our flight to the Pole, we followed Scott's route very closely. Without having known that he had done it—beyond a shadow of a doubt—I wouldn't have believed it. The fact is almost too incredible to accept.

The tragic irony of the Scott expedition was that Scott and his four companions all died on the trip back from the Pole. Evans and Oates died heroically, early on the return trip; while Scott, Wilson, and Bowers died of cold and starvation just 11 miles from a cache of food and fuel. Their frozen bodies were found the following year by a tearful party of friends, along with Scott's diary, the final entry of which read:

"I do not regret this journey, which has shown that Englishmen can endure hardships, help one another, and meet death with as great a fortitude as ever in the past. We took risks; we knew we took them; things have come out against us, and therefore we have no cause for complaint, but bow to the will of Providence, determined still to do our best to the last . . . Had we lived, I should have had a tale to tell of the hardihood, endurance, and courage of my companions, which would have stirred the heart of every Englishman. These rough notes and our dead bodies must tell the tale . . ."

The fact that the three men died only 11 miles from supplies and safety, knowing the distance to be that short, is some indication of the strain of Antarctic travel. These men, who had walked nearly 1500 miles, couldn't walk 11 more, though they knew it to be a matter of life and death. Such is the Antarctic—she will allow so much, and then no more. She has the final say in all things.

Official U.S. Navy Photograph

Inside Scott's last hut today.

Amundsen, of course, survived and returned to the Arctic, his first love and chief interest. In that area he continued his work of exploration, turning eventually to the lighter-than-air ship. On June 17, 1928, he left on a mission aboard a conventional aircraft to rescue survivors of General Nobile's airship *Italia*, which had been wrecked while returning from the North Pole. The Italian expedition had been following the line of Amundsen's earlier flight in the airship *Norge*. The Norwegian was never heard from again. What the Antarctic failed to do, the Arctic accomplished. Amundsen and Scott, who had raced each other for glory, ended up 16 years apart, entombed at the exact opposite ends of the earth, each in eternal snow and ice.

One final irony remains to be told in connection with the saga of these two men. We will never know if either of them actually stood at the South Pole! Even today, with our advanced scientific instruments, we can't reach agreement on the *exact* location of the Pole. But it doesn't really matter—they both came close enough. It does seem a little bitter, however, to think they went through so much and may have missed by yards.

After the great Amundsen-Scott race for the Pole, Antarctic exploration maintained a decidedly international character. In 1911, Lieutenant Chobu Shirase, aboard the *Kainan Maru*, led Japan's first expedition to the great Southland. In the same year, Dr. Wilhelm Filchner, on his ship, *Deutschland*, led a German expedition which made history by getting trapped in the ice for 9 months and surviving. They had, we are told, a cold and lonely time of it.

The Norwegians appeared on the scene in 1911, in 1912, and again in 1913 on an Antarctic vessel inappropriately named *Polynesia*. Between 1911 and 1914, Sir Douglas Mawson conducted a particularly productive expedition from his ship *Aurora*. No less than five major surveys were conducted by this great explorer. In 1912, the first daisy appeared in Antarctica—it was the ship *Daisy*—and carried an American sealing and whaling expedition as well as a trained naturalist.

It was the period 1914–1916, however, that saw one of the great sagas of the Antarctic acted out against a background of terrible hardship and monumental courage. The tale of Sir Ernest Shackleton and the *Endurance* is second only, in all of Antarctic lore, to the story of Amundsen and Scott.

Ernest Henry Shackleton was truly a man of Antarctica. In reviewing his life, it would seem that most of his 48 years were spent on the ice, or in preparation to go there. Born in Kilkee, Ireland, in 1874, he entered the merchant marine after college. By the time he was 27 he was, as we have pointed out, Scott's lieutenant on his first expedition. Although he was returned home because of illness in 1903, he was leading his own expedition aboard the *Nimrod* in 1907. He is reported to have reached a point within 97 miles of the Pole. Up until Amundsen made it to the Pole one month short of two years later, this was probably the southernmost point that had ever been attained.

Shackleton, back in England in 1909, was knighted and set about planning his next expedition. He left England in 1914 on the *Endurance* and was back in 1917. Four years later, he was off again on his last trip. At sea, off South Georgia Island, on January 5, 1922, he succumbed to a heart attack following a bout with influenza. He was buried on that bleak southern island. This determined and intrepid man spent the better part of 12 years on Antarctic expeditions—25 per cent of his total life. At least as many more years were spent in planning and active preparation for these four trips of exploration, three of which he led himself. Whatever the sum of his life's accomplishments may have been, it is for his great courage, strength, and leadership during the expedition of 1914–1916 that he is known, honored, and enshrined in the Antarctic hall of fame.

The first ship chosen for the expedition was the *Aurora,* Sir Douglas Mawson's stout and sturdy vessel of the contemporary sealing type. The other was built under the name *Polaris* by Lars Christensen, head of a Norwegian whaling empire.

The Shackleton family motto was *Fortitudine Vincimus*—"By endurance we conquer"—and the *Polaris* was, accordingly, renamed *Endurance.* She had been designed originally as a sort of cruise ship to carry wealthy Europeans on polar-bear hunts in the Arctic. Her career in the hands of Shackleton was shorter than it probably would have been had she been used for her original purpose, but her glory and renown were far greater.

The appearance of the *Endurance* befitted her status in history. She was a beautiful barquentine with three masts. Her 350-h.p. steam engine used coal for fuel, and her top speed was slightly in excess of 10 knots. In his remarkable account of this voyage, *Endurance* (McGraw-Hill, 1959), Alfred Lansing says of Shackleton's ship, ". . . though her sleek black hull looked from the outside like that of any other vessel of a comparable size, it was not.

"Her keel members were 4 pieces of solid oak, one above the other, adding up to a total thickness of 7 feet 1 inch. Her sides were made

Plaque placed by New Zealand government on Scott's last hut.

from oak and Norwegian mountain fir, and they varied in thickness from about 18 inches to more than 2½ feet. Outside this planking, to keep her from being chafed by the ice, there was a sheathing from stem to stern of greenheart, a wood so heavy it weighs more than solid iron and so tough that it cannot be worked with ordinary tools. Her frames were not only double-thick, ranging from 9¼ to 11 inches, but they were double in number, compared with a conventional vessel."

There can be little doubt that this 144-ft. beauty was one of the sturdiest wooden ships ever constructed. She marked the closing of a ship-building era, being, perhaps, the last of her kind. Few, if any, wooden ships designed for polar use were built after 1912, the year of the launching of the *Endurance*, née *Polaris*.

On December 5, 1914, the *Endurance* sailed south from South Georgia Island—destination Weddell Sea. Norwegian whalers at the station on South Georgia cautioned Shackleton before he left. They told him that the Weddell Sea was beset by particularly severe ice conditions. The Weddell Sea is almost circular and is all or in part

29

Sir Ernest Shackleton

British Information Services

enclosed on three sides by land: the South Sandwich Islands on the east, the Palmer Peninsula on the west, and the continent itself a cup to the south.

Two days after *Endurance* had cleared South Georgia's Cumberland Bay, she encountered the first light ice. It was replaced in a matter of hours by heavy pack ice, and a whole night was spent looking for a lead that would carry them beyond the pack. Progress was extremely slow, and 19 days after she had left South Georgia, *Endurance* was still north of the Antarctic Circle. Their lack of progress was a warning that was not heeded.

After Christmas and until the middle of January, the ice menace seemed to abate somewhat, and progress was good. They had been negotiating loose pack ice and, with a reasonable amount of caution, were never in real trouble.

On January 16, a gale struck. The gale seemed to blow itself out by January 18, and now progress seemed to give good omen. Before the day was out, however, the *Endurance* was a prisoner of the ice. She never again knew the joy and freedom of the open seas.

What had evidently happened was that the incalculably large mass of ice which floats on the Weddell Sea had pressed in tight against the mainland as a result of the northeast gale the *Endurance* had encountered on January 16. When the *Endurance* became lodged in this ice, she was just off, and a little southwest of, an area of Queen Maud Land known as the Caird Coast, named by Shackleton for his patron.

Since the *Endurance* was so far to the south when she was trapped, she had, in effect, the whole weight of the Weddell Sea's vast ice cover pressing in on her. The weight of ice was not actually resting on the timbers of the *Endurance*—not yet, at any rate—but for all the freedom she knew, that might as well have been the case. It is safe to say that no source of power known, then or now, could have extricated the wooden ship from her trap. Between Shackleton and freedom were billions of tons of ice of every description. Fresh bay ice formed in the open water leads as quickly as they were seen; a thick mushy soup of brash ice pulled at the ship like molasses; there was a vast field of solid pack ice, behind which Shackleton had pushed the *Endurance*. Great bergs spotted the surface for hundreds of miles to the north. To the south, the coast of the continent was locked behind the great Filchner Ice Barrier, impenetrable and immovable. The *Endurance* was beset forever.

From January 18 until October 27—for over 9 months—Shackleton and his men aboard the *Endurance* drifted with the ice, first southward and then to the northwest, for a total of 573 miles. Actually, the mileage was probably greater because the course on which they were helplessly carried was erratic and wove in and out, and even in circles, as storms played games with the drifting field of ice. Winter came and went with its eternal night and merciless weather extremes.

In the spring of 1915, on October 27 to be exact, it became obvious beyond all possible doubt that the *Endurance* was doomed. The ice was through with its cat-and-mouse game. The *Endurance* now had to die. With mighty pressure beyond our ability to calculate, the ice crushed in, and the *Endurance* was abandoned. Shackleton and his men took what they could from the stricken vessel and made

31

camp on the surrounding ice. Day by day, hour by hour, the tortured ship died in agony. Masts collapsed, decks burst upward, water flowed in, and yet the *Endurance* hung on. It wasn't until November 21, more than three weeks later, that the ice finally closed in over the ship on which so much had depended. We can guess at the feelings those lonely men must have had as they watched their vessel disappear for all time.

It was obvious to Shackleton that, whether they were on the *Endurance* or in the camp on the ice, they were moving northward with the ice. Finally, on December 23, they set out by sledge. Shortly after crossing the Antarctic Circle, they encountered a vicious South Atlantic gale. On January 1, 1916, they pitched camp almost at the northern boundary of the solid ice pack and drifted with this camp until April 9, when they took to their boats. On March 9, a month before they launched their open whaleboats, they felt the ocean swell beneath the ice and knew that they had drifted into the even more treacherous loose pack ice. A new hazard then presented itself—the danger that, at any moment, the ice beneath their feet or sleeping bodies might open and dump them into the sea.

When they launched their boats on April 9, they were within sight of Elephant Island, a bleak and hostile island 28 miles long and 15 miles wide lying in the eastern part of the South Shetlands. The sea was not done with them, however, and their drift turned to the southeast, carrying them away from the first dry land on which they had had a chance to set foot since December 5, 1914. The sea had its little joke, and on April 12, 1916, the drift changed again to the northwest, and three days later the weary, frostbitten men came ashore on Elephant Island.

Camp was made on an isolated rocky beach at the foot of massive and unscalable cliffs. The ship's carpenter readied one of their open boats, and nine days later Shackleton set sail with a skeleton crew of five plus himself. From April 24 to May 10, these six men sailed an open whaleboat nearly 800 miles, through some of the most treacherous ocean in the world, to King Haakon Bay, South Georgia. Cyclonic winds, driving sleet, and huge crashing waves beset them on what must be one of the great sea voyages of all time from the points of view of hardship, endurance, and skill.

One more seemingly insurmountable obstacle lay between the men of the *Endurance* and safety. King Haakon Bay lay across 20-mile-wide South Georgia from Grytviken at Stromness Bay, the only settlement on the island. They were no longer able to launch their boat to sail around to the whaling station, so it became necessary to cross over the island to get help. The trouble was, no one had ever done it. It was thought impossible!

Leaving three men behind, Shackleton and two companions added a major mountain-climbing exploit to an already incredible list of achievements. On foot, without charts or aids of any kind, exhausted, starving, and frostbitten, this small party of men blazed a new over-land trail across glacial terrain tortured into deadly crevasses by its own plastic nature. Tough whaling men, who could scale ice-en-crusted rigging on a madly gyrating ship in the midst of a hurricane, had ruled out this over-ice journey as too difficult to attempt. The island's interior was unexplored until Shackleton and his companions finally made the traverse. It was nearly 40 years before this crossing was accomplished again—this time by a party of expert climbers, fresh and properly equipped, and *they* nearly didn't make it!

Once again we are forced to speculate on the boundaries of human endurance. Even as recently as 40 years ago, nutrition wasn't what it is now. As children, these men couldn't have had the medical and the nutritional advantages available today. As adults, these men had been hammered by fate and unyielding elements to a point actually impossible to imagine. Where did these iron men get their strength and courage? What magical substance is poured into the mold that shapes a few men in each generation? Are these select few a special product of our species, born to set a pace and give other men a comparative goal? These questions must arise again and again as we survey the history of exploration in the land of ice.

At Grytviken, Shackleton chartered the whaler *Southern Sky* and made an unsuccessful attempt to rescue his men. The Uruguayan trawler *Istituto de Pesca* and the British schooner *Emma* also failed to get through to the 22 stranded men. Finally, on August 30, 1916, the sea-going tug *Yelcho,* loaned to Shackleton by the government of Chile, got through to the desperate group. It need only be added that the expedition's other ship, *Aurora,* also encountered savage ice conditions and was damaged before returning to New Zealand.

To say that Ernest Shackleton and his men performed miracles is to understate the case. One long series of incredible feats constitute one more brilliant chapter in the saga of man in the Antarctic.

The near-tragedy of the Shackleton expedition seemed to increase man's determination to conquer the southern continent. From 1920 on, expeditions set forth at the rate of three, four, and five a year. The British launched a long series of technical studies of the whales of these southern waters and their environment, known as the Discovery Investigations. The name of the ship *Discovery* gave the series its name. Nearly every branch of the still new science of oceanography was employed. Each year saw the addition of new facts and techniques that were to form the backbone of later scientific expeditions. Not only had man come south of 66° South to stay, he had come with weapons and understanding. The fierce old lady of the south would still torture and kill, but her fight to retain her secrets had become a losing battle. Man had caught hold and was never again to let go. This titanic wrestling match is still going on.

In 1928, a man came to Antarctica who would brook none of her nonsense. He had already made a mark for himself by being the first man to fly to the North Pole (1926) and by flying the first load of transatlantic mail from New York to Ver-sur-Mer, France, where he crash-landed in the surf (1927).

Rear Admiral Richard Evelyn Byrd, U.S.N., was an expert at handling tough old ladies with ice on their backs. From 1928 on, the name Admiral Byrd became synonymous with Antarctic exploration.

Byrd's first crack at the ice-age continent lasted from 1928 to 1930. He used two ships, the *City of New York* and the *Eleanor Bolling*, and three aircraft. He brought back a wealth of information and laid the groundwork for later exploits.

The years 1933 to 1935 saw the Admiral back again with two new ships, the *Bear of Oakland* and the *Jacob Ruppert*, and a long list of new exploratory projects. His live radio broadcasts to America kept a nation glued to their receivers on many an occasion. A whole nation participated, emotionally at least, for the first time.

Whatever the scientific results of the second Byrd expedition might have been, it is best remembered for the fact that it nearly cost Byrd his life. He decided, for a number of reasons, to winter alone in a shoe-box of a hut far inland, or more correctly "in-ice," from his base camp at Little America on the Ross Ice Shelf. At Advance Base, in the dead of winter, he was nearly overcome by carbon monoxide gas generated by his heating unit. Although nearly dead from these poisonous fumes, he refused to call for help, knowing that his men at Little America would respond and come after him in the eternal night of the Antarctic winter. To do so, they would have had blindly to traverse treacherous crevasse areas and be exposed to the violent winter-weather extremes. His regular scheduled radio contact with his party began to suffer because Byrd's growing weakness made it difficult, and at times impossible, for him to crank the hand generator. The men at Little America became more and more concerned as it became obvious that their leader was in great dif-

Rear Admiral Richard E. Byrd, USN

ficulty. At last, three men set out and effected yet one more miraculous rescue, in the face of the worst Antarctica could offer. Add the names Poulter, Demas, and Waite to the list of men who faced the ordeal of Antarctica and who prevailed.

In the period 1939–1941, Byrd was back, once again, with the *Bear* and the *North Star*. His long and difficult aerial surveys, and the most advanced scientific techniques yet attempted in Antarctica, successfully unlocked many more of her secrets. This expedition is marked by the careful, workmanlike scheduling and interweaving of a host of scientific projects.

In 1946 and 1947, Admiral Byrd and Rear Admiral Richard H. Cruzen led 13 ships of Task Force 68 in the U.S. Navy's Operation Highjump. It was far and away the most massive assault ever made against the bastion of ice and snow. An aircraft carrier and a submarine were even included in the contest. The main objectives of the expedition were to test equipment and train men under polar conditions. The sciences were not neglected, however, and a broad spectrum of research work was carried out.

Admiral Byrd was appointed commander of the United States International Geophysical Year (IGY) Antarctic Expedition in 1955. Later in the same year, he was placed in charge of the entire U.S. Antarctic program. In December of 1955, he arrived in Antarctica for the fifth time. Three months after his arrival, ill health forced the 68-year-old explorer to return to the United States where he died 13 months later. He never saw the results of the greatest scientific expedition of all time—the Antarctic Program of the International Geophysical Year, to the foundations of which he had contributed so much. This one man had directed the mapping of more than 1,000,000 square miles of formerly unknown territory. Add to this astounding record his exploits as an aviator and as an Arctic explorer, and you have the measure of a great man.

During the years of Admiral Byrd's activities in the Antarctic, 1928–1956, many more men of great purpose turned their attention southward: Sir Hubert Wilkins, Sir Douglas Mawson, Lincoln Ellsworth, V. E. Fuchs, and many, many more. Men of a dozen nations chipped away at the ice barrier that locked in the secrets of the South. [Permit here a blanket apology to be made to all the men whose names do not appear on these pages. Many of these men were heroes just as much as Scott, Amundsen, Shackleton, and Byrd were heroes; but space could not possibly permit even the listing of their names, much less of their exploits.]

From July 1, 1957 to December 31, 1958, more than 60,000 scientists participated in the most extraordinary cooperative venture ever known—the IGY—the International Geophysical Year. Sixty-six nations participated, and there was hardly an area on this planet that wasn't scrutinized in a way and to a degree never before attempted. All the sciences of land, sea, and sky were brought to bear on the single problem of getting to know our environment and the forces that shape it better than ever in the past. The Antarctic received a full measure of attention. And the end of the IGY did not end international cooperation in Antarctic studies—they are still going on.

The U.S. Navy was assigned the task of logistic support for the civilian IGY scientists assigned to Antarctic studies. The mammoth operation was known then, as it is now, as Operation Deep Freeze —Task Force 43. Admiral Byrd was the first to be assigned to the project, as we have seen; he was later replaced by Rear Admiral George Dufek, who later retired and handed his hat to Rear Admiral David M. Tyree, who is still in command at the time of this writing.

Operation Deep Freeze I, 1955–1956, was charged with the responsibility of advance planning and initial establishment of advance bases. Operation Deep Freeze II, 1956–1957, picked up where No. 1 left off, and so on right up to today. The American program, started in 1955, is still in full swing, and there is no end in sight. Unfortunately, 8 men died in Operations Deep Freeze I and II despite all of the precautions taken and the fantastic array of modern equipment and techniques utilized. Some 5,322 men survived the same two operational seasons. Antarctica was still to put up a vicious battle.

Today, Task Force 43, Operation Deep Freeze, is still charged with the logistic support of all United States activities in Antarctica. The National Science Foundation provides funds for and administers United States scientific research in that area through the United States Antarctic Research Program (USARP). The scientific work is accomplished by researchers from colleges, universities, and government agencies working under NSF grants and coordination.

All in all, 66 IGY stations were established in the Antarctic by 12 nations. The table on pages 38-39 gives a complete list.

It is interesting to note the diversity of studies pursued. The table below shows this spread, as seen at U.S. installations alone.

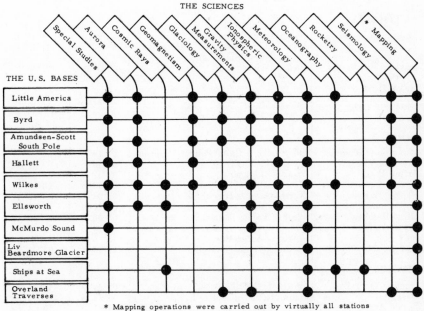

* Mapping operations were carried out by virtually all stations and traverses as an adjunct to assigned programs.

U.S. ANTARCTIC PROGRAM
I. G. Y. 1957-1958

Name of Base	Location	Latitude	Longitude
UNITED STATES BASES			
NAF, McMurdo Sound	On Ross Island: Antarctic West coast	77°51′ S	166°37′ E
Little America V	Eastern end of Ross Ice Shelf: Ross Sea, West coast of Antarctica	78°11′ S	162°10′ W
Byrd	Marie Byrd Land Polar Plateau	79°59′ S	120°01′ W
Amundsen-Scott South Pole	Geographic South Pole	90°00′ S	—
Wilkes	Coast of Wilkes Land, Indian-Antarctic Basin	66°15′ S	110°32′ E
Hallett (Jointly with New Zealand)	Coast of Victoria Land, South of New Zealand	72°18′ S	170°18′ E
Ellsworth	Edith Ronne Land, Weddell Sea	77°43′ S	41°08′ W
NAAF, Liv	Beardmore Glacier, Ross Sea	83°17′ S	175°45′ E
ARGENTINA			
General Belgrano	Coast of Weddell Sea	78°02′ S	37°48′ W
Orcadas	Island Station Mouth of Weddell Sea	60°45′ S	44°43′ W
Melchior	Palmer Peninsula area	64°19′ S	62°59′ W
Primero de Mayo	Palmer Peninsula area	62°59′ S	60°42′ W
San Martin	Palmer Peninsula area	68°08′ S	67°07′ W
Almirante Brown	Palmer Peninsula area	64°53′ S	62°52′ W
Esperanza	Palmer Peninsula area	63°24′ S	56°59′ W
Teniente Camara	Palmer Peninsula area	62°36′ S	59°57′ W
Ushuaia	Tierra Del Fuego Island: Southeast South America (Extra-Antarctic)	54°48′ S	69°19′ W
Rio Grande	Southeast South America (Extra-Antarctic)	53°48′ S	67°47′ W
AUSTRALIA			
Macquarie Island	Southeast of Tasmania	54°29′ S	158°58′ E
Mawson	Coast Station between Wilkes Land and Queen Maud Land	67°36′ S	62°53′ E
Davis	East of Wilkes Land	68°35′ S	77°59′ E
BELGIUM			
King Baudoin	Queen Maud Land coast, South of Africa	70°26′ S	24°19′ E
CHILE			
Bernardo O'Higgins	Off Northern tip of Palmer Peninsula	63°19′ S	57°54′ W
Gonzalez Videla	Southwest of O'Higgins	64°49′ S	62°51′ W
Arturo Prat	West of O'Higgins	62°29′ S	59°38′ W
Aguirre Cerda	Northwest of O'Higgins	62°56′ S	60°36′ W
Yankee Bay	Northwest of O'Higgins	62°32′ S	59°49′ W
Coppermine Cove	Close to Yankee Bay	62°22′ S	59°45′ W
Diego Ramirez	West of Palmer Peninsula	65°30′ S	68°45′ W
Punta Arenas	On Brunswick Peninsula in Chile, (Extra-Antarctic)	53°10′ S	70°55′ W
Evangelistas	In Chile (Extra-Antarctic)	52°25′ S	74°55′ W
FRANCE			
Dumont D'Urville	On coast of Wilkes Land	66°40′ S	140°01′ E
Charcot	Inland from Dumont D'Urville	69°22′ S	139°02′ E
Iles de Kerguelen	South Indian Ocean (Extra-Antarctic)	49°21′ S	70°04′ E

Name of Base	Location	Latitude	Longitude
JAPAN			
Showa (Abandoned 1958)	Queen Maud Land coast	69°00′ S	39°35′ E
NEW ZEALAND *			
Scott	Ross Island, 3 mi. from U.S. McMurdo NAF	77°51′ S	166°45′ E
Hallett (Jointly with U.S.)	South of New Zealand	72°18′ S	170°18′ E
Christchurch	Headquarters in New Zealand on South Island (Extra-Antarctic)		
Invercargill	On South Island, New Zealand (Extra-Antarctic)		
Campbell Island	Part of New Zealand (Extra-Antarctic)		
NORWAY			
Princess Martha Coast	Coast, East of Weddell Sea	70°30′ S	02°32′ W
UNION of SOUTH AFRICA			
Marion Island	South of East Africa (Extra-Antarctic)	46°53′ S	37°52′ E
Tristan Island	South Atlantic (Extra-Antarctic	37°03′ S	12°19′ W
Gough Island	South Atlantic (Extra-Antarctic)	40°19′ S	9°51′ W
UNITED KINGDOM			
Halley Bay	Coatsland, Weddell Sea	75°31′ S	26°36′ W
"A" Port Lockroy	Palmer Peninsula	64°50′ S	63°31′ W
"B" Deception Island	Palmer Peninsula	62°59′ S	60°34′ W
"D" Hope Bay	Palmer Peninsula	63°24′ S	56°59′ W
"F" Argentine Island	Palmer Peninsula	65°15′ S	64°16′ W
"G" Admiralty Bay	Palmer Peninsula area	62°05′ S	58°25′ W
"H" Signy Island	Weddell Sea	60°43′ S	45°36′ W
"J" Ferin Head	Palmer Peninsula	66°00′ S	65°24′ W
"N" Anvers Island	Palmer Peninsula	64°45′ S	64°05′ W
"O" Danco Coast	Palmer Peninsula	64°44′ S	62°32′ W
"W" Loubet Coast	Palmer Peninsula	66°54′ S	66°48′ W
"Y" Horseshoe Island	Palmer Peninsula	67°49′ S	67°17′ W
Port Stanley	South Atlantic (Extra-Antarctic)	51°42′ S	57°52′ W
South Georgia	South Atlantic (Extra-Antarctic)	54°16′ S	36°30′ W
South Ice (Abandoned 1958)	Polar Plateau	81°56′ S	29°30′ W
Shackleton	Coatsland, Weddell Sea	77°57′ S	37°16′ W
U.S.S.R.			
Mirny	Coast of Davis Sea	66°33′ S	93°01′ E
Oazis	Knox Coast	66°16′ S	100°44′ E
Pionerskaya	Interior, Wilkes Land	69°44′ S	95°30′ E
Komsomolskaya	Interior, Wilkes Land	72°08′ S	96°35′ E
Vostok	High on Polar Plateau	78°00′ S	110°00′ E
Sovietskaya	High on Polar Plateau	78°00′ S	88°00′ E

* Of the five bases listed for New Zealand, only Scott and Hallett were actually located in the Antarctic.

Official U.S. Navy Photograph

A huge Russian tractor arrives at U.S. South Pole base for a three day visit.

Each of the 12 nations participating in the gigantic undertaking accepted a clearly defined area of responsibility, not only geographically, but also within the sciences. Rapid exchange of data was, and is, accomplished by a huge network of radio communications. It was found, however, that even the most advanced equipment and techniques could not overcome the magnetic caprices of Antarctic storms. Even the scientists of the atomic era talk with each other only with the permission of the Old Lady of the South.

The United States holds strictly to a treaty she signed with 11 other nations on December 1, 1959. This treaty guarantees non-militarization of Antarctica and freedom of scientific investigation. The full text of the treaty appears as an Appendix to this book.

The U.S. Navy in the Antarctic today has no weapons. The few rifles in American hands on the ice belong to civilian scientists who use them to collect specimens. There are no locked file cabinets; there is no security restriction. A cold war may rage elsewhere, but in the coldest part of the world it is replaced with warm cooperation. A Russian base may radio in at any time and ask for technical details of American scientific investigation or for weather data, and the answer is immediate and complete. They have never been known to refuse the extension of the same courtesies.

The United States neither makes nor recognizes territorial claims in Antarctica. It is an international laboratory, and it is a strange and happy contradiction of our times that the world's fifth largest continent should be free of national boundaries and border guards. Russians visit American stations for extended stays, and Americans learn to drink vodka in the long winter night at Russian installations. It may, one day, turn out that the biggest single contribution Antarctica makes to the human race is the knowledge that, once he is united in honest purpose, man can live and work with his fellows.

Official U.S. Navy Photograph

U.S. Navy humor in Antarctica.

41

Official U.S. Navy Photograph

P2V-7 Neptune in flight over the Beardmore Glacier.

   This unprecedented international cooperation is absolutely essential to the achievement of the goals that have been set—the complete investigation of Antarctica. No one nation, however rich, could possibly afford the cost involved. No one nation has the genius to do it alone. On the ice, at least, men seem to have found the answer to living in the world.

   A visit to an Operation Deep Freeze installation today presents a bewildering kaleidoscope of impressions. Men of every sort are constantly on the move: a dental technician cleaning his equipment at three in the morning, a United States Admiral, a couple of youngsters from the Midwest comparing their beards with those in photographs of the old-time explorers, and a ham radio operator contacting a buddy in Delaware who will put a phone connection or patch through to an apartment in Brooklyn to see whether the detachment cook is a father yet. In shacks and huts, scientists watch the gyrations of an octopus in an aquarium maintained to match the temperature of the water under the ice from which it came, or check a cosmic-ray recorder; they make chemical tests on rock samples brought in by field parties and correlate data collected on the progress of the glaciers in their thundering march to the sea. Balloons are released with miniature radio transmitters that will send back information about the weather high above the ice. Helicopters transport investigators to areas of study over difficult terrain; and thundering cargo planes, the largest in the world, prepare airdrops of equipment and supplies for inland stations. The noise and apparent confusion go on 24 hours a day, 7 days a week. Inside a snug and cozy hut, Jimmy Darren and Wolfgang Amadeus Mozart contend with each other over separate hi-fi systems, while, outside, Navy construction specialists blast massive, gaping holes into a rocky slope in preparation for a nuclear power plant being assembled in Baltimore, Maryland, by the Martin Marietta Corporation.

The bewildering array of men, equipment, and nature appears to be utter chaos personified. Actually, it is a steady march forward by a group of men, military and civilian, toward a goal that has taunted mankind for too long—the final solution to the riddle of our environment. We can't help but wonder what a Bellingshausen or a Scott or a Palmer would think of Task Force 43 and Operation Deep Freeze. Some things they would recognize: men bundled against the cold, the sweet joy of a hot meal and a warm bed after 10 hours' hard labor in the snow and ice, the sad reminder of an occasional flag-draped coffin awaiting shipment home that the Antarctic can still lash out and destroy the enemies of her age-old secrecy. For the rest of it, I would wager that they would be as bewildered as we will be when we visit our great-grandchildren's housing development on the moon. Exploration south of 66° South has come a long, long way. It has just as far, at least, yet to go. The stubborn witch of the bitter night and flesh-destroying frost is down but not out.

4

Ice

Ours is truly a water planet. This simple chemical compound, two atoms of hydrogen wedded to a single oxygen atom, is one of the most widely distributed and abundant substances known. It is an absolutely essential constituent in the cells of every living thing. No animal or plant can be free of water for a single instant and live. Water outside of an organism may be expendable temporarily, but never inside. Many minerals contain water within their crystals. It has been estimated that the Earth's atmosphere weighs 5,633,000,000,000,000 tons, and much of this vast mass of matter is water.

In this chapter, when we speak of water in its various forms, we will speak of it at sea level. Changes in altitudes, and therefore in pressure, to some degree alter the behavioral characteristics of this important chemical. We are concerned with it, in this book, as it occurs in a fairly narrow altitude band with the center at sea level.

Taking into consideration the known range of measurable temperatures, water is a liquid throughout a relatively narrow stretch in the spectrum. Above 100° C (or 212° F) it is a gas, and below 0° C (32° F) it is a solid. Since temperatures can be produced that range several hundred degrees below 0 and thousands of degrees above 100, the 100 centigrade degrees wherein water can remain a

44

liquid seem quite unimpressive. Since life depends so entirely on water in the liquid form, it is hardly a coincidence that most life thrives within that 100-degree band.

We seldom encounter pure water, for water absorbs solids and gases alike with great ease. When we find water collected together in a natural body, we find water that has fallen or flowed and collected foreign matter during its course. If it has flowed over land, it has collected solid matter from the surfaces it bathed. If it has fallen as rain, it has collected carbon dioxide, chlorides, sulfates, nitrates, and ammonia, along with organic and inorganic dust on the way down. Wherever it sits, its surface continues the unending process of accumulating impurities. Snow is almost certainly the purest natural source of water we know.

The water in the great seas and oceans contains 3.5 per cent, by weight, of dissolved impurities. Principally, this surprising percentage consists of $NaCl$, $MgCl_2$, $MgSO_4$, $CaSO_4$, and KCl. *All* known natural chemical elements, however, can be found in sea water, at least in traces.

We are concerned here with water in just its solid forms, as snow and ice. Ice and snow create some of the most beautiful sights on this planet. Snow has been a symbol of purity since time immemorial, and ice has often been thought a great luxury in many parts of the world. Vistas of ice and snow may inspire men to art and prayer with their beauty, and ice may cool our drinks and preserve our foods; but together, they create one of the most frustrating substances on Earth.

Ice is terrifyingly destructive and uncontrollable, often horrifyingly petulant, and it has, on more than one occasion, reduced strong and brave men to tears. Ice can gobble up a city, a ship, a plane, or a man with equal ease. Nothing affects it very much, except temperature; and although the temperature required can be produced by a cigarette lighter, the amount of heat needed to make much of a dent is not available to man in portable form. When man wants to do something about snow and ice, he has physically to move it around. This can be accomplished by back-breaking labor, terribly expensive machinery, or generally impractical explosives. When ice really gets moving, man has no choice but to get out of the way. Since ice has chopped the top off more than one mountain and crushed more than one continent into a totally new shape, the picture of a man pushing and shoving back is pretty silly. With the right kind of equipment, man can get along pretty well on top of the ice; but as to controlling its movement, he might just as well

The frozen edge of an ice-age continent—the Bellingshausen Sea.

try to cork a volcano or change the oceans' tides with a couple of canoe paddles!

Ice, as we will be discussing in later chapters, appears to be in a natural balance. There has to be a certain amount of ice in the world, or there won't be much land. Ice is apparently nature's way of keeping water out of circulation. As we saw in Chapter 1, the Antarctic is the great frozen reservoir at this particular time. Although we aren't exactly certain why nature has to keep a frozen reserve, or why the position of that reservoir switches around from time to time, we do know where it is now, and we are learning to get along with it; and we seem to have accepted the fact that we (and not it) will have to change, unless we want to surrender more of our planet to its clutches than we can spare.

Only a fool would make firm declarations as to what the limits of man's technical abilities will one day be. If man can go to the moon (and it is now obvious that he can), he very well may, one day, come up with a portable energy source with which he can melt all the ice he wants. Not the least frustrating thing about ice is that, should man one day develop this capability, he won't be able to use it to any great extent—not unless he is considerably more fond of swimming than he is now. The better course appears to be living with it and not fighting it. The first step toward survival is understanding. So let's see what we know about these deadly beautiful substances that occur where water and freezing temperatures come together.

The first thing we must acknowledge in our discussion of the properties and characteristics of ice is that, despite its extremely low melting point, it is not always a temporary condition. While iron melts at 1535° C, carbon at 3500°, and tungsten at 3370°, ice starts to melt at just a small fraction of a degree above 0. Still, there are parts of the world in which ice can remain more or less as a permanent condition. "Permanent" can be a relative term, and we use it here in the sense that it denotes a passage of time without change that far exceeds human memory. The Arctic is one part of the world where ice is a permanent condition. Although these great northern lands surrounding the Arctic Ocean are jungles in the summer, as compared with the Antarctic, ice is always present, even though invisible. In the Antarctic, the surface ice is always there, and you can never forget for an instant that you are at the very end of the world. In the Arctic, very much in contrast, the scene is relatively lush. Rabbits, foxes, caribou (reindeer), lemmings (small mouse-like rodents), an exceedingly rich parade of bird life, and hundreds of kinds of flowering plants fill the scene with movement and vivid color. Nature runs wild for a few brief weeks. Yet, the ice is there. To find it, you have to dig, and what you find is ice thousands of years old. For a few feet, your shovel cuts through a mushy, spongy turf, and then ice!—cold, hard as low-grade concrete, and unyielding to the sun that, only inches away, fills the world with a riot of floral color nurtured by its life-giving warmth. You may encounter ice mixed with soil; ice mixed with humus; or pure, hard, blue ice. Flowering meadows called tundra, thundering caribou herds—the whole rich panorama of the Arctic summer sits on ice. If that ice ever melted, the whole scene would sink into a swamp and disappear, as billions of tons of liberated water rose to the surface and froze there, concealing, perhaps forever, a world of life and beauty. Millions of square miles of our Earth sit poised on endless fields of permanent subterranean ice.

What else can we say about ice? It isn't just a brittle substance

47

Ice forms on the superstructure of the USS GLACIER.

that cools our drinks or denudes a continent of life. Ice is a vital, plastic substance with amazing properties. It exists long before we see it as a complex molecule carried in solution in water, much like salt in the sea. Steam and water vapor consist of a simple molecule known as hydrol; water is composed of double molecules called dihydrol; while ice is made up of triple molecules called trihydrol. Dihydrol, or water, contains a percentage of the triple molecules, and these increase in quantity as the temperature of the solution drops from the boiling point down toward the freezing point. Before actually congealing at the freezing point, the triple molecules are in solution. At 0° C, the flow of heat out of the solution is sufficient to allow a trihydrol saturation, and the trihydrol precipitates out of solution, and—BANG!—a solid!

Under a microscope, this first ice is without crystal form and appears as small disk-like particles—as a *colloid*. These colloid particles flocculate and grow, passing through a stage where they are half colloid and half crystal, until the true ice crystals appear. The form of these first crystals depends on the nature of the water and ranges from feathery snow-like structures in quiet water to broken

48

Official U.S. Navy Photograph

Crevasse in pressure-ridge area.

spicules or spines in agitated water. But, in either case, this cloudy mass soon congeals into the buoyant mass of floating ice with which we are all familiar.

Even after ice has formed on the ocean to a depth of 4 or 5 inches, it is mushy and springy. It rides up and down with the swells and wavelets like a soggy canvas covering thrown over the sea. Ice formed on fresh water to the same depth is quite firm and hard. The difference appears to be due to that 3.5 per cent of salts in the sea. Trapped between ice crystals (it can't be trapped *in* them), this salt mass is slower than the trihydrol molecules in taking its place as part of a solid field.

The properties of ice, once it has formed, are truly remarkable. Although it is a better conductor of heat than water or snow, ice still functions as a protective blanket against extremely cold temperatures. A good way to keep heat loss down in a bitter cold environment is to provide a coat of ice! As early as 1871, a scientist in Bologna, named G. A. Bianconi, was pushing rods and perforated plates into masses of ice and watching the *solid ice* exude through the openings. Ice is plastic. It is exceedingly hard between $-40°$ C and around $-9°$; but between $-9°$ and 0 it is relatively soft and plastic. Equally amazing is the fact that ice is, to some degree, elastic. It doesn't exactly snap like a rubber band, but it does have a measurable elasticity.

Along with its plasticity and elasticity goes ice's viscosity. It does have the ability to flow, as witness the glaciers. A coefficient of viscosity has been determined, and the point at which ice will crack or shear can be predicted. Ice has a definite tensile strength and a given compressibility. The crushing strength of ice has been given as ranging from 327 to 1,000 pounds per square inch. It has been pointed out that 1.5 inches of solid ice floating on water will support a man; 4 to 6 inches will support horses and wagons; and 18 inches, a railroad train!

Strangely enough, although natural water is a good conductor of electricity, ice is a good insulator. The explanation for this gets pretty technical and need not be enlarged upon here. Similarly, the density, heat of fusion, latent heat of vaporization, specific heat, and vapor pressure have all been studied extensively, but really interest only the specialist.

Before going on to note the different kinds of ice, we should acknowledge that the subject of this discussion is no simple substance. That little clear cube that we manufacture with such ease in the freezing compartment of our refrigerator is really quite remarkable. Whether it serves to cool a glass of lemonade or looms out of a black fog in a frigid sea to rip open a ship and bring death and terror in its wake, ice is a substance of some importance to man.

The first plane ever to land at the South Pole—buried in snow back on the Ross Ice Shelf.

The lip of a crevasse.

Official U.S. Navy Photograph

Official U.S. Navy Photograph
On Otter over an open crevasse.

When water vapor floating in the free air of the atmosphere precipitates out and crystallizes, we call it snow. In all of nature, there are no more beautiful forms. They generally are hexagonal patterns, and their variations are endless. It is generally accepted that no other mineral achieves the variety of crystalline forms known of snow. By the time snow particles reach the ground, they may be in the form of tiny crystals no more than 0.005 inch across, known as *diamond dust;* or they can range upward to cottony flakes or plates several inches in diameter. This latter form is really a complex aggregate of crystals. In areas of great snowfall *and* accumulation, these delicate and intricate masterpieces soon lose their angular form and *firnicate,* or become rounded through age and compression. The result of this compression and of wind compaction is ice—ice derived from the atmosphere. When this occurs at high altitudes, as it so often does, the final product is the *glacier.* The product of the glacier is, in turn, the *floating ice shelf* and the *iceberg.*

The sculpturing power of the glacier is, indeed, prodigious. Where glaciers fail to meet the sea and melt away on land, great *moraines* are found. These piles of rock, soil, clay, and other debris give testimony to the power the glacier has over the land it covers. Billions of tons of surface material are scooped up and carted off. *Glacial striations* on rock surfaces show the route the glacier traveled. Debris, caught up in the bottom of the glacier, gouge tracks in solid granite. Boulders the size of a 20-room house have been collected and carried off by these great flowing masses. Flying over high mountains, you will inevitably note bowl-like amphitheaters cut into the sides of the individual ridges and peaks. These are known as *cirques* and have been cut by glaciers. When these glacier-cut cirques fill with water during warmer times and become lakes, they are known as *tarns*. Small glaciers feed into the larger flows, much as tributaries flow into rivers. If the great glacier eventually scoops out a deeper trough, these branches are left as *hanging valleys*. Some of the great spectacular waterfalls have appeared as a result of these hanging valleys.

There are essentially two kinds of glaciers; the *continental glacier*, such as now exists in Greenland and Antarctica, overriding hills and valleys alike, and the *valley glacier* found in most high mountainous areas. Rocky ridges between valley glaciers are known as *arêtes*, while rocky outcrops in continental glaciers are called *nunataks*. When a glaciated valley flows into the sea and partially submerges,

Hummocky sea ice.

National Academy of Sciences

A weasel trapped in soft snow.

the *fiord* results. Geology textbooks contain dozens of terms to describe the effects glaciers have had on the world's landscapes. (Once again, let us state that it is not within the scope of this book to exhaust the terminology of one specialty. It is, however, a fascinating study.)

Let us go back to the forms of ice as it is derived from the atmosphere. We are familiar with snow and the great variety of incredibly beautiful forms it takes. When snow falls through a mass of water droplets in the process of freezing while still aloft, the crystals pick up a coating of *rime*, and the snowflakes, no longer recognizable, are variously known as *graupel, soft hail, snow grains,* or *tapioca snow. Rime,* as we encounter it on the ground, is a coating of feathery or stippled opaque ice from freezing fog or water droplets. It is sometimes incorrectly called *hoarfrost,* which is really defined as a silvery-white deposit of *ice needles* formed during still, clear nights. When falling rain encounters freezing temperatures, Americans refer to it as *glaze* or *sleet*, while in England it is called *glazed frost*. In England and most of Europe, *sleet* is taken to mean a mixture of snow and rain.

Before going on to look at ice as we find it on land and on sea, we should note one other atmospheric phenomenon, *frost smoke*. This ghostly effect occurs when cold air flows across warmer surface waters. Fog-like clouds drift up from the water in a weird panorama. The effect is eerie, to say the least.

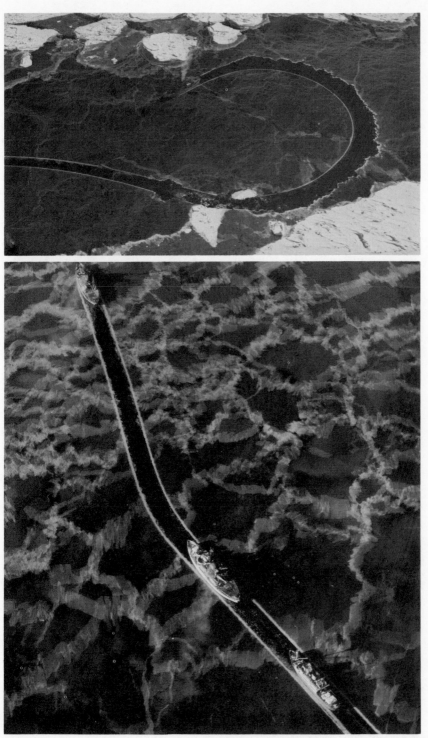

Official U.S. Navy Photograph

U.S. Navy ships negotiating young sea ice.

Snow can form in layers when the periods between heavy falls are periods of extreme cold, of high winds, or of long duration. This is commonly known as *stratified snow*. As the snow ages or becomes *firn snow*, it can take on a granular quality and become known as *névé*. It is denser in this form than when it fell. If winds are exceedingly high, the top 6 inches or so can form into a *windcrust*. This layer, with the crystals tightly compacted, is quite hard and can take the weight of a man without showing a mark. It makes a strange creaking sound as you walk on it and gives the impression of being hollow underneath. In unexplored areas, where crevasses may be a danger, the effect can be downright unnerving. This author encountered windcrust in the vicinity of the South Pole, in an area quite free of crevasses, but remembers well the strange sensation of walking across an endless field of snow totally unyielding to 200 pounds of man and equipment. The best word I can find to describe the sensation is "expectant." It makes you feel as if something is about to happen. Happily, there is no particular hazard connected with this phenomenon, except where it is coincident with a *snow bridge* over a crevasse or when you fall against a broken edge of crust. The latter can give a mean bruise or cut.

A really strange state of affairs, peculiar to areas of permanent snow, high winds, and extreme cold, is *sastrugi*. This is an area of wind-driven, fluted ridges of snow, from inches to 5 feet in height. The ridges, actually windcrust on more or less vertical snow forma-

Frozen sea ice provides a natural dock after the ice-breakers have been to work.

Official U.S. Navy Photograph

tions, are extremely hard. A powerful snow plow snapped its hardened-steel blade in an effort to level a sastrugi area, on at least one occasion known to the author. Such areas are extremely rough on aircraft attempting to land and take off. For sledge teams, dogs and men alike, these ridges, looking for all the world like rolling waves at sea, can make travel all but totally impossible. In a similar vein, *wind bretts* are slabs of hard, wind-packed snow.

If a glacier doesn't suffer *ablation* or melting and wearing away, it eventually reaches an altitude where great changes occur. In the Antarctic, it usually feeds the great floating *ice shelves.* An ice shelf is a vast mass of floating ice that is either fed by glaciers or accumulated by permanent freezing, or both. When this shelf feeds out over coastal land, with the sea to the front and mountains to the rear, it is known as an *ice piedmont* or *piedmont glacier.* An *ice sheet* is a mass of ice and snow in excess of 20,000 square miles in area!

The seaward face of these great ice shelves is known as an *ice wall* or *ice barrier,* and is generally very steep and often quite high. When a field of this ice extends around an island or along a large stretch of continental coastline, it is called an *ice belt.* When a field is caught between two headlands or is firmly attached to the shore, it is sometimes referred to as *land ice* or *fast ice.* Occasionally, the floating ice is forced offshore by winds blowing out to sea, and open water forms between it and the coast. The resultant channel is a *shore lead.* A *lead* or *lane* is a navigable path through floating ice. If it forms as an open water lake, it is called a *polyna.*

And so, our icy vocabulary continues. These strange and often totally unfamiliar words are the everyday working language of the men who are opening a part of the world that, up to now, has been locked in frozen mysteries for which words didn't even exist. Each new venture man undertakes requires new communication tools. To cite a few, the space age has brought "gantry," "orbit," "escape velocity," and "A-OK" into our language, just as the supermarket has given us terms like "check-out counter" and "green stamps." Nothing daunted, the world of ice and snow has given us more new words without which it is extremely difficult, if not impossible, to reasonably communicate ideas about matters frigid.

Glaciers or ice barriers facing the sea eventually *calf,* dumping massive ice chunks loose to float away or run aground. The *iceberg* is born—and so is a whole new vocabulary. A *tabular berg* is a flat-topped island of ice, broken free from a flat ice shelf. It can be of absolutely astounding proportions and, as stated elsewhere, one was found the size of Connecticut! The action of the sea, its rise and fall, is generally responsible for the *calving* process. If the berg is less than 30 feet across and less than 15 feet above sea level, it is given the engaging and quite logical name of *bergy bit*. A piece smaller than a bergy bit, almost awash generally, is called a *growler*. When a berg *rots* and starts to disintegrate, as the result of warmer weather or ocean currents, *brash ice* is found. This is nothing more than the wreckage of other ice forms and quite often refreezes and compacts into a new *field* or *floe*. A *floe* is sometimes a piece of free sea ice, a *light floe* being 3 feet or less in thickness, a *heavy floe* being thicker. Either kind of floe can be many miles in diameter. An accumulation of floes and brash ice is also called a floe, as well as a *pack*. These packs are played upon by wind, tides, and currents, and can be dangerously deceptive. False leads form only to close again after ships have started down the garden path. A blind alley and little room for making a turn are frequently the result. Disintegrating sea ice, known as *rotten ice,* is also frequently a constituent of these packs. A cold snap, or a wind shift moving the mass into more frigid conditions, arrests the process of disintegration, and the end result is a holy mess!

When one floe rides up on another, the result is called *rafting* or *rafted ice*. The *pressure ridges* formed, also called *hummocks,* are murder for the man on foot. Blind crevasses lead down into open water, and foot travel is hazardous in the extreme. We shall have more to say about this in the next chapter. Pressure ridges also occur where outflowing land-fed ice meets inflowing sea-ice head on. The noises in such areas, caused by the buckling and exploding upward, can be haunting.

There are just a few more quick definitions needed to complete our working frigid vocabulary and free us to proceed. *Bay ice* is ice of recent formation found in sheltered coastal areas. The *albedo,* as we shall discuss later on, is the reflecting power of a surface; and *anchor ice* is ice without a real albedo. Also known as *ground ice, bottom ice, ground gru, lappered ice, glace du fond, grundeis,* and *moutonne,* it is ice forming attached to the bottom of a river, a stream, or a pond. After all that, we probably won't be encountering it in the Antarctic, since there is a shortage of streams or ponds in which it can form.

When ice first starts to form in a body of water, while the particles are still fine, invisible, and with little or no buoyancy, it is known delightfully as *frazil ice* or, even better, as *lolly ice*. And that is our icy vocabulary!

Before dropping the subject temporarily, some mention must be made of the fact that tricks with pressure and temperature can be used to create different kinds of ice—different grades, as it were. Experts number these from five to eight varieties, but since the differences involved constitute a technical matter that is not really our concern here, we shall let this nod in that direction suffice. Also, of course, we have hardly exhausted the subject of ice and snow. A good library shelf could be filled with the technical studies that have been done, and the surface has hardly been scratched. For our purposes, however, I think we have enough information on hand.

ICE! Blue, cold, dangerous, and beautiful—a miracle of nature, a freak of cold environments—does a special vocabulary really describe you? NO! Ice is an experience, not just a substance. Ice is a way of life and a way of death. Ice is a preserver and a destroyer. What the stars are to the astronomer and the open sky to the pilot, ice is to the polar explorer and scientist. To understand ice, you have to adore it (or you could never live with it) and you have to fear it (or you would never survive it). Let's explore this world of ice . . .

5

How to Survive an Ice Age

THE Antarctic is a place of incredible beauty and unrelenting hostility. The entire continent sits poised like a loaded gun waiting for the stranger to make a single mistake; and every visitor to this part of the world is a stranger. The consequence of error has too often been death.

More likely than not, your first approach to the Antarctic today would be by air. The air lanes are open long before sea routes are free of ice; and after the seas begin to freeze over again in the fall, planes can still make some flights. Unlike most areas of comparable size, there is no land approach—you can't even come close on foot.

Air travel in the Antarctic has become a matter of course with the advent of long-range, high-altitude aircraft and sophisticated electronic equipment. It may be commonplace, but it will always carry with it a measure of hazard. The Antarctic is too unpredictable and too remote a mistress to permit anyone to be casual in his dealings with her. Between 1946 and 1961, 22 Americans died in 7 air accidents in Antarctica. Even this sad fact, however, is a brilliant tribute to Navy and Air Force pilots and crews who, in just a third of that time alone, from 1956 to 1961, operated 224 aircraft and flew thousands of hours. They carried tens of thousands of tons of supplies and equipment. The record of military aviation on the ice is staggering in its achievement, but 22 lives were claimed by Antarctica as tribute and as a reminder that the ice is still her realm.

Let us take an imaginary flight between Christchurch, New Zealand, the jumping-off point for the continent, and McMurdo Sound and see what we might encounter. This trip has been made hundreds of times in the past few years by the U.S. Navy and Air Force, in support of scientific research. It is now considered a routine flight.

If we make the flight in October or November, we might travel on a huge Air Force C-124 Globemaster or on a Navy C-130 Hercules. The Hercules is ski-equipped and can fly throughout the season, which runs from late September to February or early March. If we go much beyond November, use of the Globemaster will be out of the question because this huge flying silo cannot be equipped with skis and must make her landing on the hard surface of the sea ice. By early to mid-December, summer in the southern Hemisphere, the sea ice around McMurdo Sound will be too soft to trust with the massive weight of the monster C-124. The Hercules, on the other hand, can land on the permanently frozen, snow-covered Ross Ice Shelf as long as the weather holds.

The trip from Christchurch to McMurdo Sound is approximately 2,200 miles, and virtually all of this will be over the roughest ocean in the world. Aside from the very remote possibility of an ice breaker, we will probably encounter no other surface or air traffic. We will

The landing strip at McMurdo Sound.

Official U.S. Navy Photograph

Official U.S. Navy Photograph

New Zealand dog team and a U.S. Navy C-130BL Hercules on sea-ice at McMurdo Sound.

be alone over an ocean running 40-foot waves as a matter of course and whipped by vicious, freezing winds. If our aircraft should go down in these seas, our chances of survival are practically nonexistent. If the plane doesn't break up in the high seas immediately upon impact, there *is* a chance of getting a rubber inflatable raft into the water. If we get dunked in the process, we have an estimated four minutes to live. These freezing seas suck vital heat and energy out of a human body the way a sponge soaks up water. Even if we survive long enough to launch ourselves from our sinking plane in a rubber raft, we will be faced with the unbelievable isolation of thousands of miles of open water. The temperatures and the freezing ocean spray are severe enough to kill a man in a matter of days, or even hours. It would be possible to survive, one might speculate, but it is highly unlikely.

Let us be optimistic, however, and assume that our plane will not come down in the ocean. How can we prepare ourselves for our arrival at McMurdo Sound?

We start by wearing the basic first two layers of our special polar clothing at takeoff. As we approach the Antarctic, the flight engineer will slowly but steadily drop the temperature within the aircraft until it approaches the surface temperature at our destination. By the time we arrive at McMurdo Sound, we will be wearing our outer cold-weather gear. In this way, our bodies will not suffer severe shock from the change when we deplane. Our bodies might overreact if we carried New Zealand's temperate climate with us all the way south in the pressurized interior of our aircraft.

There are some things that might go wrong before we actually set down on the ice. A magnetic storm might come up suddenly, knocking out all communications. We would not be able to make contact with New Zealand or McMurdo Sound. We wouldn't know what to expect at our destination.

A condition known as "white-out" might occur. If that happened, our pilot would be unable to take his aircraft down until the situation cleared. White-out is a strange condition caused by low cloud cover and snow crystals. It destroys all shadows and depth perception. It is impossible to judge distances and make out specific shapes, even in rough outline. It is like moving through a bowl of milk. There was a story, some time ago, that, during a white-out, a helicopter crewman, thinking his vehicle had landed, stepped out while still a hundred feet in the air. Luckily, as the story goes, another crewman realized his error in time to grab him and save his life. I have been unable to verify this story, but it creates an accurate impression, be it fact or fiction.

One factor is to our advantage: we won't have to land in the dark. We will have sun 24 hours a day. However, this also works against Antarctic operations, since long seasons of light are balanced with long seasons of darkness, when air travel is not practical.

Our aircraft has survived the 10- to 13-hour flight, and we are on the ice. Whether we are scientists or tourists, we are not going to be satisfied with sitting at the edge of the continent. Sooner or later, we will have to make our way inland. The chances are that we will travel by air. If we go from McMurdo Sound to the South Pole, we will be flying between two snow-covered landing strips, one at sea level and one 9,600 feet in the air. We will fly over mountains, along the routes of the glaciers, and will always be subject to a possible magnetic storm or a white-out condition. The capabilities of our aircraft and the skills of our crewmen will be sorely tried by the incredibly difficult problems of maintenance. Hydraulic systems are affected severely by prolonged exposure to temperature extremes and rough snow landings. There are no hangars in the Antarctic, so maintenance is carried out, even in sub-zero temperatures, on open sheets of ice. If there is any situation conducive to human error, it is this. It is a miracle and an ever-lasting tribute to the members of our Armed Forces that any plane manages to fly under these conditions.

At the South Pole, our plane will deposit us, along with its other cargo, and take off with a maximum of 20 minutes on the snow. During these 20 minutes, the engines will not be shut off. If they were, it would be next to impossible to get them started again without auxiliary equipment. The 4 huge engines will churn up the snow surface as long as the plane sits down. A minor blizzard will be worked up by this massive movement of air and add to the already uncomfortable environment.

On our plane we will carry a 3-month supply of food for each passenger and crew member. Regulations are very strict about this —it must be done. We will also carry tents, sleds, portable radio equipment, medical supplies, signal devices, and all manner of survival apparatus, for if our plane were to go down during the flight, and if we were to survive, it might be a long time before weather permitted rescue. If we came down in an area where normal landings and take-offs were not possible, we might have to trek many miles to a place where we could be taken out in safety. The range of the helicopter is limited, and we might be too far for even this great life-saving device to reach us.

Let us suppose that the ground crew and the flight engineers have accomplished the difficult task of maintaining our aircraft in perfect condition. We have not been besieged by magnetic storms, white-out conditions, or a blizzard at our destination. Communications and radar have functioned perfectly. The terrible turbulence, the high winds, and the sudden updrafts from mountains and glaciers have not affected us too adversely. We have landed at our destination, high on the polar plateau, without having to resort to emergency procedures or equipment. It is now time to travel overland.

Aircraft are virtually indispensable to modern exploration. The highly developed skills of aerial photography and map making can save science months and (when working with short seasons, as in the Antarctic) even years in charting a new area. For all this, explorers still must go overland to make seismic readings, collect mineral samples, measure wind velocity and temperature at the surface, and perform the myriad other tasks that are part and parcel of modern scientific exploration. Overland it is.

Walking is not very practical in the Antarctic, and the romantic dog-sled of old, although still in use, is hardly suited for long traverses of investigation requiring heavy and complicated equipment. We will probably use a Snowcat, a heavy-duty vehicle with 4 independent tracks on pontoons. This powerful device will carry us great distances with relative ease, if not in luxurious comfort.

64

It carries its own radio equipment and can pull sleds carrying enormous loads. It is the limousine and the hot-rod of the Antarctic.

On this journey, we will be carrying far more food than we expect to use. If a breakdown occurs and we are forced to remain in isolation for longer than anticipated, we will need this food to stay alive. Between 5,000 and 6,000 calories a day per man will do it—that's more than twice as much as a large man needs under normal circumstances.

We will carry medical equipment, and if we are going to be gone very long, it would be a good idea to take a doctor along. We will carry tons of high explosives. Periodically, charges will be set off near the surface of the ice, so that our instruments can measure the time lapse between the explosion and its echo from the rock bed beneath the ice. In this way, the thickness of the ice cap can be charted accurately and the ground contour mapped carefully. Valleys and mountain chains that were totally unknown have been discovered this way both in the Antarctic and in Greenland. We will carry meteorological equipment to record details of temperature, wind, and humidity. We will have equipment to measure the Earth's magnetic field, and also gravity measuring devices. We will need equipment to collect ice samples, so that the age of the ice cap can be determined; and we will be equipped to make celestial observations. A variety of photographic equipment will be at our command, and we will release high-altitude balloons carrying tiny radio transmitters to supply us with data about wind, temperature, humidity, and air pressure high over the ice.

One of the heaviest and bulkiest materials we will carry is fuel. Our powerful Snowcats aren't very economical to operate, and we will need fuel for heat and cooking. One of our biggest problems will be water. There is none to be had, unless we melt snow and ice, and this takes valuable fuel. It takes 3 *tons* of snow to make 1 cubic yard of water! We will have to use fuel to melt this snow or carry water with us. We won't take many hot baths on this trip! Although there are untold thousands of billions of tons of frozen water in the Antarctic, it is a desert. Our need for water will be increased by the fact that the humidity is about the equivalent of that over a burning desert of sand. Our lips and cuticles will crack from dryness, and our throats will be parched.

Since this is a well-planned expedition, large aircraft will play leapfrog with us and deposit caches of fuel and other supplies along our proposed route of march. Unless something goes wrong, we will keep close to our planned itinerary and find these air-dropped

A large Snow Cat caught by the rear tracks in a crevasse. That's a crevasse detector in front!

caches waiting at predetermined points. We couldn't carry enough fuel for a long trip, so these air drops are essential. The drop crews have become so expert that they could parachute tractors to us if necessary. We will also carry a complete set of tools and spare parts for our vehicles, for drive shafts and clutch assemblies have a hard time of it on the ice.

What are the big problems, then? Ice travel is affected as adversely by magnetic storms and white-out conditions as air traffic. In addition to these phenomena, there are the inevitable blizzards. We must be prepared, on one or more occasions during our trip, to sit for 2 or 3 days at a time, waiting for the hurricane-force blizzards to pass. It would be insanity to continue our trip while a blizzard was tearing up the surface into blinding clouds of snow. During these blizzards, the temperature will drop severely, and winds of seemingly impossible velocity will blow unabated for hours on end. Every tiny crack and crevice in our vehicles will permit the furiously wind-driven snow to get in. We will have to really button up, if we want to be comfortable at all. When the blizzard is finally over, an hour or a week after it has started, we will have to dig out. This could take several days, for the drifting can amount to many tons. While we are sitting in wait for the storm to run its course, we will have to be extremely careful about running any equipment or heating devices that give off fumes: carbon monoxide is a deadly enemy in cramped quarters.

Something else we will have to fear is fire. If we set a vehicle or a shelter on fire, we may die from exposure *if* we survive the flames. With no water on hand and with terrible winds blowing, any fire will race out of control in a matter of seconds. This is particularly so, since everything is bone-dry from the lack of humidity. Fire is such a menace that it has been said that heat, not cold, is the great hazard of the Antarctic.

We should mention one other thing about the wind—its effect on our bodies. Someone has calculated that 1 knot of wind has the equivalent effect, on the human body, of 1 degree of frost. That means that a temperature of 60° below zero and a wind blowing at 100 miles an hour will have the same effect on a person as a temperature of 160° below zero. The equivalence figure of 1 knot of wind to 1 degree of frost is not accepted universally as being completely accurate, but it does give an indication of what the wind can do to you. In the Antarctic, when the wind blows, you go under cover! Bare skin, exposed for any length of time, will suffer frost bite. An unfortunate number of ears and noses have been sacrificed to the cruel winds of the Antarctic.

We have survived all of this; what other problems might we encounter? Ice is a plastic substance and, although seemingly as hard as steel when met on impact, it does, in fact, flow like water. Depending on a number of factors not yet fully understood, the rate of flow can vary from inches to yards a day! Billions upon untold billions of tons of dense ice on the move—something has to give!

Each winter, the sea freezes and pushes its own massive sheets of ice up against the ice sheet that has formed on the land from compressed snow and is flowing toward the sea. Two irresistible forces meet, and a tremendous upheaval occurs. Pressure ridges form, and mountains of jagged ice burst upward from the level plain, creating nightmarish ice obstacles. The sound alone is terrifying. There are essential hazards involved in negotiating a pressure ridge area. It is extremely difficult, and at times all but impossible, not to slip, stumble, and fall. Since many of these ridges tower 20 and 30 feet into the air, there is the constant danger of broken bones and torn ligaments and muscles. At home, a broken leg can be reason to send a humorous get-well card to a friend, but in the Antarctic, a broken leg is reason to summon all available emergency rescue techniques. Just one misstep, a fall, a broken leg, and a man could die of exposure, lying helpless on the ice. That is one good reason why you don't travel alone in the Antarctic!

While working outside in extreme cold, great care must be taken

67

Trapped and disintegrating iceberg.

to avoid heavy exertion. When the temperature is really down, heavy breathing can cause the lungs to bleed; and while this isn't necessarily a fatal condition, it is painful and requires hospitalization. The "don'ts" of the Antarctic form a long, but exceedingly important, list. The margin for error is about as thin as the razor's edge upon which man skates while on the ice.

The Antarctic hazard that is perhaps best known is the crevasse. These great, yawning trenches and caverns occur quite naturally in a pressure-ridge area, on the downward flowing glaciers, and, seemingly inexplicably, in certain areas of the flat plateau. Actually, a crevasse is a sign that the ice is on the move, that great, irresistible forces are at work. A crevasse would not be so much of a hazard if it could be seen, but too often they are invisible. Drifting snow, adhering to the rims of a crevasse, soon forms a light snowbridge that crusts over. Generally, it is indistinguishable from the surrounding snowscape.

The weight of a tracked vehicle or, frequently, just that of a man or a dog-sled, can cause this bridge to give way suddenly, without warning. Some of these crevasses are only inches wide, and a sprained ankle is the result. Sometimes, however, these crevasses can be many yards across and hundreds, or even thousands, of feet deep. There are ridges and ledges on the sides of many crevasses, and men have survived incredible falls by what appear to be sheer miracles. As a safety precaution, men on foot, in known crevasse areas, tie themselves together. When the going is particularly hazardous, the lead man prods ahead with a long pole, looking for weak spots. Progress is slow in such areas.

What do we do when we're in a heavy Snowcat in unknown territory? Our lead "cat" will push a strange rig in front of it known as a crevasse detector. This is nothing more than a large boom pushing a series of metal dishes to the front and side. A current passes through these discs, forming an electric field beneath the surface. If the detector passes over a break in the ice, the electric field will be interrupted and register on an instrument in the cab. Not foolproof, it is, however, highly effective and virtually essential to overland travel in vehicles heavy enough to crash through almost any snowbridge encountered.

If, for some reason, crevasse detectors aren't employed, and the area is suspected of being dangerous, there is another alternative. A lead "cat" is sent along ahead *empty!* The crew walks behind it, controlling its speed and direction with long remote-control cables. It is just like many children's toys; only the game is a rather deadly one, and the walk across the ice behind a lumbering "cat" is not exactly child's play. But, then, nothing in the Antarctic is.

Since many crevasses are miles long, it can prove to be impractical to go around them. Explosives are lowered into the open trench and set off at various levels. The concussion collapses the walls of the crevasse, and some work with a plow can generally fill in an area wide enough to act as a bridge. It is slow, cold, tedious but, at times, essential work.

One more problem with which we will have to contend is snowblindness. The glare can be painfully punishing. A man can go temporarily blind in a very short time if he fails to wear his special glasses or goggles. Regular sunglasses are not, generally, satisfactory. Sunburn is also a hazard. Snow and ice form a highly reflective surface.

We have outlined a number of hazards that are a normal part of Antarctic exploration and travel, but there is yet one more that is all-important. It is the product of the combination of other factors we have discussed, and that hazard is psychological.

The Antarctic takes a great deal out of man. It doesn't allow him to make errors. It forces him to stay in extremely close quarters with other men, making privacy virtually unobtainable. He is forced to go for months without mail; and he is denied all normal communication with the civilized world, except when he can arrange a phone patch with a cooperative ham radio operator. The regimen of 24 hours of sunlight and 24 hours of darkness takes its toll of a man's normal orientation to the habitable world. Insomnia frequently results. Men in the Antarctic are uncomfortable most of the time. Sanitation is extremely difficult, and most luxuries are missing. Men work, very often, at unhealthy altitudes and tire easily. Small, petty arguments and disagreements assume terrible proportions. Men have cracked under the strain, and even suicides have resulted. Bleakness, eternal bleakness, is a bitter pill to swallow. A normal, healthy man can survive all this, as long as he is not forced by his own mental attitude to become careless and commit errors in his working and living environment. If he does make mistakes, the Antarctic is waiting. Even in her passive moods, when she is not actively out to get you with her frightful extremes, she sits waiting for misjudgment, miscalculation, and misbehavior.

We have flown to the Antarctic and we have flown over it. We have also gone overland. Let's now retrace our steps and imagine that we are approaching the Antarctic in the classic manner, from the sea. As we have said, the Antarctic Ocean, completely surrounding the continent, is the most turbulent sea in the world. Great cold currents, rivers within the ocean, stream northward from ice-locked shores and dip down under the warmer water of the North and form the 20- to 30-mile-wide turbulent Antarctic convergence. The route south is generally described as passing through "the roaring forties, the furious fifties, on beyond the screaming sixties." The numbers, of course, refer to the degrees of latitude. The Antarctic Circle, as we have pointed out, is at 66½° S, the South Pole at 90° S, the Equator is 00°. If we are aboard a ship, one thing that will absorb our attention from the moment we approach these waters is the iceberg. Man has not yet devised an instrument that can have any appreciable effect on one of these great floating islands of ice. An atomic bomb would hardly make a dent; so, by comparison, it is easy to calculate what would happen if our ship plowed into one. In 1958, the U.S. Navy measured an iceberg that was 56 miles wide and 208 miles long—a cake of ice as large as Connecticut! Some of these great bergs tower hundreds of feet into the air and, since seven eighths of a berg is beneath the surface, it is easy to imagine what the total size must be. Take an ice cube and float it in a bowl of water, and you will see what an iceberg is like.

Icebreaker USS GLACIER.

There are two kinds of icebergs, essentially, and both occur in Antarctic waters by the thousands and the tens of thousands. There are the great, flat-topped, tabular bergs that break off the floating ice shelves and the jagged "castles" that are torn loose from an area where pressure ridges form or where land ice feeds directly into the sea. These bergs are magnificent to see, but they create a floating hell for ships in storm-tossed and fog-shrouded seas. Collision with one of these bergs means a pretty rough jolt and possibly extensive damage. It is like plowing into a wall of low-grade concrete.

Besides icebergs, we will encounter thinner floes of loose ice broken off from frozen seas farther south. These offer no particular problem to the icebreaker, and even the thin-skinned cargo ship can negotiate with safety if reasonable care is taken. Particular attention must be paid to our stern end, however, because floes that won't damage a hull at reasonable speeds can destroy our screws. The Antarctic Ocean is no place to be with bent and twisted propellers that can shake a drive shaft loose within the hull of a ship.

The spray will freeze on our decks, rails, and superstructure. The whole ship will be caked. Great care must be taken in walking about the wildly dancing decks. Everything we do on the exposed parts of our ship will be made infinitely more difficult by the constant build-up of ice. We will chip and scrape until our arms are numb, but, still, the ice will mount in thickness. We will know that we are getting close to the Antarctic continent!

One good thing, though—our icebreaker can't be crushed by the

71

ice like the *Endurance.* Her hull is so shaped that, should the pressure approach dangerous proportions, she will ride up out of the ice and escape the grip of the pack.

Our icebreaker is equipped with a device that can pump many tons of water from one side of the ship to the other in just 90 seconds. This shifting weight causes the vessel to tilt, or heel over. This heeling, coupled with the dish-shaped hull and powerful engines, will enable our skipper to rock and shove us out of anything we encounter—a far cry from the days of sail and splintered wooden hulls!

One nice thing about icebergs, besides the fact that they are beautiful to look at and a photographer's dream, is that they supply wonderful fizz water. Drop a chip of iceberg into an ordinary glass of water, and escaping air bubbles delightfully. It is interesting to note that the air so released may be many, many centuries old.

There aren't too many more nice things to be said for these floating nightmares.

Like everything else that is used in the Antarctic, clothing has a job to do. It is not just a matter of heaping a lot of wool, fur, or cotton on your back, but a carefully analyzed job-to-tool relationship. What are the tasks that Antarctic gear must perform? They can be broken down this way:

1. Keep Warmth In

The human body creates a measurable amount of heat by the chemical breakdown of the fuel (food) fed into it. If this heat is controlled in its natural tendency to radiate itself into an environment whose temperature is far lower than that of the body itself, it will stay at the level required for life. If the heat escapes too rapidly, the body will be unable to replace it fast enough to guarantee survival, no matter how much fuel is fed in. The body can produce just so much heat in a given period of time, and this absolutely essential heat must be controlled very carefully. The inner layers of clothing perform this task. A mass of heavy wool won't do the job. Clothing must be loose and must consist of a number of layers that permit air spaces to form. Air is a great insulator, and where it is maintained by the body at body temperature, the stove has a chance to function properly.

2. Keep Cold Out

Clothing, properly designed, manufactured, *and used,* not only will keep the body-generated heat in but also will keep the cold air

72

out. Freezing blasts of air will not only snatch away indispensable body heat, but also destroy tissue by frostbite. These cutting, frozen blasts are kept away from the body by outer clothing, designed specifically for this purpose. The fabric used is of a much tighter weave than the inner layers. These outer layers discourage the circulation of air, unlike the inner layers that actually "breathe."

3. Keep Moisture Out

Even though the Antarctic is desert-like in its humidity level, there are liquids with which man must contend: ocean water, melted snow and ice, cooking liquids and fuels, and chemicals. We have no practical clothing for Antarctic use that is completely waterproof, but a material with reasonable ability to repel moisture is used.

4. Light and Comfortable

Clothing is not a luxury in the Antarctic—it is an absolute necessity. Clothing that is too tight encourages frostbite by restricting the circulation of body-heated air and the flow of blood in surface tissues. Tight clothing, buried deep under bulky outer gear, chafes and is difficult to adjust. Since sanitation is always a problem, and baths few and far between, constant chafing by improperly designed or ill-fitted gear is a very real hazard. Skin will take just so much chafing before it splits, wears away, or blisters. Open sores, constantly being irritated, can lead to serious infections that are difficult to treat. Clothing that is too heavy causes excessive perspiring. A body that is drenching itself negates all the good done by the water-repellent outer layers in which it is wrapped. Perspiration freezes, and nothing could be more disheartening than a layer of ice on the bare skin. Badly fitted clothing can also be clumsy and cut down a man's efficiency. An inefficient man is not only excess baggage on an expedition, he is also a hazard to himself and his team-mates. Fashion experts tell us that clothing makes the man. Nowhere is this more true than in the Antarctic, because without clothing—very special clothing—man would cease to exist in this land of incredible extremes.

The U.S. Navy has developed an Antarctic wardrobe that has proved itself many thousands of times over. It is a collection of miscellaneous items that combine to make an efficient machine— machine in the sense that it has a job to do. Let's see what this gear consists of:

Nothing is more susceptible to cold injury than the feet, and nothing can make a person more miserable than wet, cold, or un-

Official U.S. Navy Photograph

A well-dressed Antarctic explorer.

comfortable footgear. The Navy has reduced the amount of foot-gear required down to two items—one pair of heavy woolen socks with cushioned soles and one pair of boots. The boot has an impermeable rubber exterior and a nylon inner lining. At various places, there are felt and wool insulating layers sealed into the rubber, and a wood shank runs from the arch back to the heel. The boot is double-laced and extremely comfortable. Each boot has an escape valve actuated by a simple pull-tab. This is used when Antarctic personnel fly at high altitudes. A simple tug on the tab, and excessive air pressure, locked into the boot at the time of dressing, leaks out. The boot is so constructed that, if ice water should get in by accident, it will heat to body temperature almost immediately. You can walk around in temperatures approaching 100° below zero and not have cold feet!

The hands are also likely victims of frostbite, and even more of a problem since they require ease of access. Basic handgear consists of a pair of heavy woolen gloves, sometimes with leather palms and fingers, and a large, dramatic-looking pair of mittens. The mittens are leather on the front and wooltuft or fur on the back. They are attached to the wearer by long straps and come halfway up the forearm, overlapping the sleeves of the jacket. When work is necessary for which mittens are too clumsy, they can be pulled off without fear of losing them. If very fine adjustments are anticipated, such as in photography, a pair of thin cotton gloves can be worn under the woolen pair. There is a hazard to hands that exists only in extreme cold—you can't touch metal. Bare skin against bare metal causes an extremely painful injury: they stick together. In pulling them apart, it is the skin that will give, and many is the inexperienced Antarctic traveler who has left a bit of himself sticking to a camera, a door handle, or a wrench. Frost-bitten hands, just as feet, are not only painful, but actually very serious. Amputations were performed with terrible frequency until the proper gear was developed.

The face is the only part of the body that is regularly exposed. In really extreme conditions, a mask is worn. It has a soft fabric interior and a hard, wind-resistant outer shell. Little trap doors snap across the mouth and the nose, making these two rather important gadgets available for blowing, wiping, and smoking. When the weather is not at its worst, or when the exposure is not too long, masks are generally not required. An exception, of course, is the case of high wind. The ever-present pair of sunglasses is worn with and without the mask, for the eyes need constant protection.

The body is protected by a series of layers, each one of which has a job to do. The maximum worn usually consists of:

1 pr. regular underwear (optional).
1 pr. waffle-weave "long Johns."
1 pr. heavy woolen trousers (inner).
1 heavy woolen shirt.
1 heavy woolen sweater.
1 pr. pants-liners, made of a synthetic fabric of light weight; buttons into the outer pants.

1 jacket-liner, of the same material and construction as the pants-liners.

1 pr. outer wind-proof, water-repellent trousers with drawstring ankles; fit over the boot-top.

1 wind-proof, water-repellent jacket with drawstring sleeves; fit under the mittens. This is a zipper jacket with a flap that snaps in position over the zipper.

1 wool-lined, peaked cap with earflaps.

2 hoods—one from the jacket-liner and one from the jacket. The one from the jacket-liner can come off and be worn separately. This latter piece of gear has a fur rim and a wool lining. The fur rim has an inner wire frame that can be bent to a snug position around the face. The outer hood is water-repellent and wind-resistant.

1 beard of various designs (optional).

There are a number of snaps, flaps, and laces to make this rig snug and really amazingly comfortable. The whole kit weighs somewhere around 30 pounds.

The beard is a subject of much discussion. You see some beauties on the ice, and I would guess that, in one week's time, you can see the last 2,000 years of beard styles on parade. Everybody seems to have his own idea of beauty, and the Antarctic affords the perfect opportunity for experimentation.

Whether the beard is a good idea or not, I don't know. Some old Antarctic hands swear by it as a protection against wind and cold. Others, with just as much time on the ice, say that the snow that gets trapped in it, and the icicles that form on it, make it more trouble than it is worth. I don't know, for although I went down with full intentions of growing a masterpiece of my own, I gave up after a few days. It got itchy!

Man can survive in the Antarctic and, as we shall discuss in a later chapter, indeed he must. Attention to detail, ability to absorb and apply the lessons already learned, and a mature attitude toward heroics are some of the keys to survival.

There are men who have faced terrible decisions, moments when calculated risks had to be taken to save the lives of others or protect the results of months of work. There have been true heroes in the Antarctic and, unfortunately, many of them are dead. In day-to-day existence on the ice, heroics are generally not called for and a deadly game to play. If you want to prove something to yourself

Snow filters in through every crack.

about yourself, do it somewhere else. Fools who shore up their masculine ego on the ice by great displays of bravado risk the lives of their fellow explorers. Many times, whole teams have had to risk their lives to extricate some poor "tough guy" from trouble he brought on himself. The man who slides down a slender rope into the yawning mouth of a crevasse to rescue an injured comrade from an ice shelf is a true hero. The risks he takes are calculated, controlled, and motivated by the best of unselfish human instincts. The braying donkey who disregards the safety precautions to prove he is "all man" doesn't deserve the consideration or concern his teammates are, unfortunately, honor-bound to give him. The number of men who have been lost because of the foolhardiness of others will never be known. Perhaps it is just as well. It should be sufficient for anyone going south to know that this can be the case. The ice is a bad place for the "hey-look-at-me" kind of guy.

The U.S. Navy, today, has rigid control over the men it selects for Antarctic duty. Men who can pass the Navy's normally strict physical and psychological requirements are not necessarily acceptable for this difficult assignment. When a man volunteers for duty on the ice (and most men there *are* volunteers), the doctors do more than listen to his heart and lungs; they listen to his soul. Motivations for volunteering are carefully weighed, and adaptability, psychological as well as physical, is carefully measured. The key to survival in the Antarctic—the master key—is not clothing, food, or equipment, but man himself.

The quality of man who has reached the ice, and the work he has accomplished in a very short time, are nothing else but miraculous. Less than 400 men, at the time of this writing, have been at the South Pole. A few stations on the ice can count the total number of visitors from the north in the thousands—a few thousand, anyway. But all the people who have ever crossed the Antarctic Circle, in all of history, brought together, would hardly fill a few apartment houses in Brooklyn. Most of these people have survived their great experience, but a few died tragically. Some of these victims died because of their own avoidable errors, but most of them perished in the process of learning right from wrong—Antarctic right from Antarctic wrong. Man has learned a great deal in his short visit to the ice-age continent. Most encouraging is the fact that he has learned enough to be able to hang on and learn the rest. Before all is said and done, the Antarctic will have its days of supremacy, and, on those days, man will pay a dreadful price; but the tide has turned, and it is clear that man's will will prevail.

6

The Mammals of Antarctica

HEN we speak of plant and animal life in the Antarctic, we can use two seemingly contradictory descriptions with complete accuracy—"the least" and "the most." While the land and ice of the continent are as devoid of life as any place on Earth, the Antarctic Ocean is quite literally the richest pasture on our planet. It has been estimated that there is more life in an acre of Antarctic Ocean than in any other acre anywhere on land or sea—even an acre of dense, steaming jungle.

The edge of the continent constantly chills the surrounding surface waters, creating an upwelling of warmer, deeper waters (colder water sinks, pushing the warmer up). These turbulent, vertical currents cause mineral sediments to rise off the bottom and remain in suspended circulation. The mineral-rich surface waters, exposed to 24-hour sunlight for a good part of the year, support tiny diatoms and other microscopic plants which reproduce by the billion billions, and these, in turn, support absolutely incredible numbers of tiny shrimp known as krill. The red krill occur in such astronomical numbers that they discolor the water for thousands of square miles. At certain times during the Antarctic summer, these waters are so rich with life that they become soupy—actually thickened by the

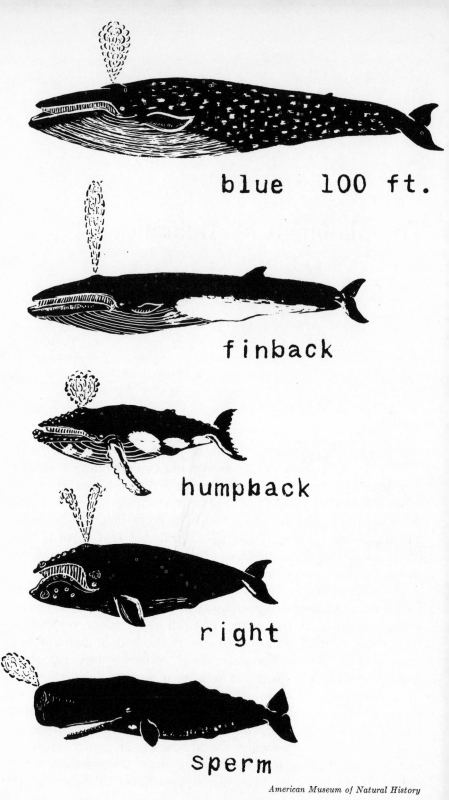

blue   100 ft.

finback

humpback

right

sperm

American Museum of Natural History

Scale drawings of five whales.

incredible mass of life. This plankton-rich sea plays host, on a seasonal basis, to the largest animals that ever lived on this planet—the mighty whales.

THE WHALES

Whales are the backbone of the only real industry the Antarctic ever had, whaling. It was, and is, of great economic importance. The history of Antarctica cannot be told, or the lure of this great area understood, without some thought and understanding of this impressive group of animals. Whales belong to an order of mammals known as the Cetacea, which includes all whales, *true* dolphins—not including the fish which is also known as a dolphin—porpoises, and animals called platanistids from tropical fresh waters. Like other mammals, the whales are warm-blooded, equipped with lungs for air breathing, and nourish their young with milk. There can be little doubt that whales are descended from land animals. They have a five-fingered, hand-like device that has been converted into a flipper. Like any dog, goat, or monkey, the members of the whale tribe maintain a constant body temperature and, in making the transition from land to marine mammal, they found that blubber under the skin better suited their purpose than hair growing out of it. Whether blubber is primarily a food-storage vault or an effective insulator is not clear. It was by this phase of their transition—the development of blubber—that the whale made man an everlasting enemy. Blubber makes the whale an important crop for man to harvest. The extent of this harvest can be judged by the fact that, during one two-hour period, off the South Shetland Islands, whalers slaughtered 1,540 Pilot whales! The Pilot is a huge dolphin measuring as much as 28 feet in length. The kind of slaughter just mentioned may soon push the Pilot whale close to extinction over much of its range.

There are two suborders of living whales. The Mystacoceti, or whalebone or baleen whales, are without teeth and feed on plankton like the rich red krill of the Antarctic coastal regions. The Odontoceti, or toothed whales, include the mighty Sperm whale, the valuable Bottlenose whales, and dolphins. Of all the whales hunted in the Antarctic, 90% are whalebone or baleen whales, mostly various rorquals and Humpbacks.

Most baby whales, which may measure up to 25 feet in length at birth, depending on the species, do not have a well-developed blubber padding. For this reason, whales migrate to warmer seas

Modern whale-killer and catch.

to bear their young. Once the young are established, the vast pods plow south or northward to the polar seas to feast on the rich plankton and other foods supported by it. It is after they reach the colder waters, where the enriched diet of unlimited krill is available to support a whole chain of marine life, that the young start to grow their thick blubber layers.

The "whalebone" we refer to is not, of course, bone at all, but rather a horny substance that forms in long, thin, triangular blades with one fringed edge, that hang from the roof of the mouth—some times as many as 600 to 800 in each whale's mouth. These blades create an extremely effective strainer, working like a half-closed, hairy venetian blind. The whale equipped with them can swim through vast fields of red shrimp, ingesting tons in a matter of minutes. The baleen whales are either fish or krill eaters, and some, like the Sei and Bryde's whales, take both. When the Antarctic visitors are in temperate seas where there is no krill, they subsist on a copepod (*Calanus finmarchicus*), which is much tinier than the Euphausiaceae or krill, and a variety of other plankton including Pelecypods, swimming, shell-less snails.

It is the need to find warm water in which to bear their young and the need to revitalize themselves on the rich Antarctic pickings that cause these great creatures to migrate vast distances each year. Their migratory routes are generally well known, and they are hunted mercilessly during their annual treks.

Among the toothless whales that regularly appear in Antarctic waters is the Humpback [*Megaptera böops* (*nodosa*)]. More than 46,000 of these great animals were taken in the 1937–1938 season alone. This 52-foot monster, with its distinctive shape, used to be a common sight, early in October, in Antarctic waters. Each year now, they are fewer and fewer, and they may be on their way to extinction; although no species of Cetacea is yet known to have become extinct in modern times. Still, man has been very unwise in his whaling economy.

One of the earliest attractions to the southern seas was the Black Right whale (*Eubalaena australis*). This large, and once plentiful, animal was pursued relentlessly during the last century. In one 13-year period, American whalers alone took 193,522 of this southern race, according to the usually accurate records of the New England whaling firms. The result of this decimation is obvious—this species has all but disappeared from the Southern oceans.

The dark-above and light-below Fin whale (also known as the Finner and Razor-back) (*Balaenoptera physalis*), the second largest of all whales and a rorqual, is still a common sight in Antarctic waters. Its 80-foot-long hulk forms the basis of modern whaling and is frequently reported by contemporary expeditions. Unless some

Norges Hvalfangstforbund
Whale being drawn aboard a factory-ship.

new and *better* measures are taken to protect it, however, this giant race will also vanish over much of its range, as so many have before.

The mightiest creature ever to live on Earth is a plankton eater and frequents the Antarctic shrimp fields during the summer months. The giant Blue whale (*Balaenoptera musculus*) has been known to reach 113 feet in length and to weigh an estimated 150 tons, although no one has yet devised a method of getting one on a bathroom scale. The number of infinitesimal "shrimp" required to sustain an animal of such incredible proportions must be astronomical.

Since speed in swimming is a result of the ratio of muscle power to friction-producing surface, when frightened the mighty Blue whale can drive its massive form through the water at great speeds. Its horizontal flukes, characteristic of the whole whale tribe, pump up and down with great force, and there can be few more exciting sights in nature than one of these true giants breaking clear of the surface and then sounding. The movement of the flukes has been described as semi-rotary, but I have been unable to discern this myself in films of whales taken under water in the open ocean. The great French underseas explorer, Captain Jacques-Yves Cousteau, had some of this whale footage in his award-winning film, *The Silent World*. Semi-rotary or straight up and down, woe to any whaleboat that ventures too close to the tail flukes of any animal 100 feet in length! These mighty propellers are not supported by bone, but by unbelievably powerful muscles, and they alone weigh tons.

Norges Hvalfangstforbund

The factory-ship.

Whales waiting to be cut-up and rendered.

Australian News & Information Bureau

Hunt-and-kill-whaling south of Australia.

A number of toothed whales also appear in the far South. These more aggressive species feed on cuttlefish, squid, octopus, and true fish. The Pilot whale or Blackfish (*Globicephalus melas*), a large dolphin, as we pointed out, appears in vast pods, but now less frequently than before. There are several beaked whales (*Ziphiidae*) and, very rarely, the 30-foot Bottlenose whale (*Hyperoodon rostratus*).

The aggressively dramatic and extremely valuable Sperm whale (*Physeter catodon*) is usually a tropical or, at least, temperate animal. On occasion, however, stragglers do appear in the far, far South. They are usually old males who have wandered off, no longer able to breed. Female Sperm whales and young appear annually in the "howling fifties," and the migration pattern of these whales is very complex. Since the Sperm whale, with his huge jaws full of immense teeth, prefers to dine on the giant squid, we can presume that some variety of this animal dwells in the depths off the Antarctic. Octopuses have been taken in nets lowered through holes in the permanent ice shelves, so the presence of squid should not be much of a surprise. Sperm whales have been known to submerge to 3,200 feet, and although, like all whales, they prefer to surface for air every 5 to 10 minutes, they reportedly can stay down for 75 minutes. The breath-holding record, incidentally, is believed to be held by the Bottlenose whale—a full 2 hours!

The legend of Jonah in the belly of the whale is resurrected periodically by the whaling man for the edification of the landlubber. It is safe to estimate that every pub, in every whaling port in the world, has seen its own Jonah invented on the spot, when the gin and the tall tales started to flow. Waggish whaling men seem to have a second profession, the amusement and amazement of the innocent.

There can be little doubt that men have been swallowed by whales. It is almost inevitable that the animal doing the swallowing would be a Sperm whale. I have seen photographs of a 34-foot squid taken from the stomach of a Sperm whale only 46 feet long. A 60-foot Sperm whale would hardly gag on a 6-foot man.

Although it is not stated as a fact, it is suggested that some men, at least, must have been taken by these furious, pain-maddened beasts. Here is where we part company with the old whaler's tale, however, for we don't believe these unfortunate men came back alive!

Dr. Egerton Y. Davis, Jr., in the year 1947, in Boston, Massachusetts, did write a letter to *Natural History* magazine, which contained what is unquestionably a true account of a man being swallowed by

a Sperm whale. It was in 1893 or 1894, and it happened in the North Atlantic. Dr. Davis was a young surgeon attached to a whaling fleet; he personally opened the stomach of the Sperm whale and removed the remains of a man who had been taken by the beast three days before. The unfortunate man's shipmates had witnessed the tragedy. It isn't necessary to go into the medical details here, but suffice it to say that the man could not have survived his experience, under any conditions.

The folk music and the folk tales of man have been greatly enriched by the creative ability of the men who pursue the whale—North and South. We must recognize our debt to them, but we must also retain our own perspective.

What the jaguar is to the Amazon basin, what the tiger is to India, and the wolf to the caribou of the Northlands, the Killer whale (*Orcinus orca*) is to Antarctica. This largest of the dolphins is the arch-killer and true villain of the sea. He is found in nearly all the major seas and oceans and is very common in the South. His appetite is voracious, and his hunt for prey both endless and merciless. Although males seldom, if ever, exceed a length of 31 feet, and females only half of that, one Killer was taken with 13 white-sided dolphins and 14 seals in its stomach. The Killer's beakless mouth is equipped with between 40 and 46 viciously curved teeth of immense size. They are as much as 2 inches in diameter. Hunting in packs like wolves, these black-and-white hulks strike like lightning; and when they happen upon an unfortunate herd of seals, they cut through the center like a gnashing hurricane. They chop the desperate animals in half and gulp down the two pieces without losing speed. The froth of foam and blood is all-too-common a sight. The young, with the yellow tinge to their characteristic white bellies, twist and turn around the edges of the panicked seal herd, crowding the escapers in toward the center, and grabbing scraps and young seals for themselves. It is utter carnage, and the unbridled ferocity of these attacks has been witnessed and even photographed. The giant 5- to 6-foot dorsal fin, in appearance not unlike a shark's, cleaves the water like a twisting periscope as the first sign of trouble. The glistening black backs undulate in and out of the ice floes, preparatory to attack. Occasional glimpses of the distinctive white slash, above and behind the mean little pig eye, give the final positive identification—these are *true* Killers.

The Killer will take what it can find—seals, penguins, and even fish—although it prefers warm-blooded creatures. A belief is held by

Official U.S. Navy Photograph

A Killer whale rising to blow.

many that the Killer, after it gulps down a seal victim whole or in two parts, flays it and disgorges the skin. This phenomenon is often recorded but, to the best of my knowledge, hasn't been confirmed.

Killers, like all the Cetacea, are believed to possess tremendous intelligence. They most often are put on a level with the dog; but this author, on two occasions, has heard it stated by known authorities that they are nearer to man—certainly on a level with the ape. For the moment, that is a moot question, and we will just say that they are as bright as they are aggressive, and that is really saying something! It is the combination of this intelligence, aggressive nature, and insatiable appetite that makes them the real terror of the sea. It is certain that they can think at least enough to improvise, as opposed to responding to pure instinct. It is certain also that they can communicate, as it is believed all Cetacea can. Their mouse-like squeaks and squeals, quite out of keeping with their size and nature, seem to carry definite messages, indicating a pack language. Let's examine some ways in which their intelligence is used to implement their frightful predisposition to mayhem.

The world's largest animal, the great Blue whale, falls victim to the Killer, only a fraction his size, because of the Killer's ability to participate in a cooperative effort. A pack of Killers (the peaceful-sounding word "pod," usually used to describe a group of two or more whales, hardly seems appropriate) will combine to dispatch the great leviathan in an ingenious display of tactics. The monster Blue is surrounded, below as well as on all sides, and pursued and worried until exhausted. It is often said that the huge Baleen whales are frightened into a kind of numbing shock by the appearance of a party of marauding Killers. This could be true. Some Killers will attach themselves to the giant's flukes and hang on like bulldogs to keep the victim from thrashing or gaining speed in the water. The rest of the pack hammer at the Blue's mouth and rip at his lips with their savage teeth until either enough of the face is torn away to expose the tongue, or the Blue opens his mouth in pain and exhaustion. The thrashing, frenzied effort to get at the unfortunate animal's tongue can be likened to the behavior of the piranha in the Amazon basin waterways. The tongue is a great delicacy, evidently, and frequently all that is consumed. The bleeding victim is left to die in agony. If you are wondering how 30-foot creatures, ravenously hungry, could be satisfied with such a dainty morsel as a tongue, just recall the proportions of the prey. In 1932, an 89-foot Blue whale, weighing an estimated 119 tons, was dissected, and it was found that the tongue alone weighed 3 tons. That is not so dainty a tid-bit,

Dr. H. E. Anthony and the skeleton of a Killer whale. Note the teeth!

and remember that an 89-foot Blue whale is still 24 feet short of the presently known maximum. Besides, there are lots of whales in the sea, and lots of tongues.

Occasionally the Killers lose out. There are authenticated records of large aggressive bulls, notably Humpback whales, standing their ground in defense of their cow and calf. Their menacing counter-charges and thrashing 15-foot flippers have disbanded the marauders, and the Killers have departed in search of less difficult prey. What the percentage of success realized by the Killer is, is not known. Whales are generally peaceful animals, but, evidently, some peaceful animals, like some peaceful people, can rise to the occasion and fight back with unsuspected fury. It may be a matter of individual personality.

The question most frequently asked concerning the Killer whale is about the danger it poses to man. It is generally accepted that they are given to attack. However, no less an expert on matters marine than Jacques-Yves Cousteau has said that, from the limited evidence at hand, he personally felt that the danger these animals pose has been overstated. He doubts many of the stories told and much of what is accepted as fact. Other writers, on less authority perhaps, have quoted wild adventures and many close shaves. It is hard to accuse all these people of fabricating. The fact that some people have found the animal dangerous, or at least potentially so, and others have found it otherwise does not necessarily make for mutually exclusive observations.

An engineer friend of mine from New York, Pete Ianuzzi, went skin-diving off the Florida Keys and encountered barracudas at close quarters, stacked up like cordwood, and didn't suffer from the experience. Yet, there are incontrovertible records of people being maimed and killed by the same toothy torpedo. Sharks do not always attack, yet they certainly are a menace to avoid. People have walked up to within 15 feet of a well-fed lion on an African plain and taken pictures in safety; yet many men, women, and children have fallen prey to this powerful cat.

The plain and simple fact is that we don't know how dangerous the Killer whale is. We do know how dangerous he could be. One case of not being molested or one of attack can't change or establish a scientific point of view in either direction. There is one special way, however, wherein the Killer can be a real menace, even if it is a mistake on his part. The Killer has a very disquieting habit of swimming beneath light ice cakes or floes and looking up for dark shadows silhouetted against the ice's translucent blue tone. When he spots these shadows, or when he surfaces near an ice floe and spots seals or penguins resting, he will dive deep beneath the cake and then shoot upward at great speed. It is known that he can fracture cakes 2 or more feet thick with his back and head. The cakes he can't break up, he tries to tip by heaving his full weight against them. Figuring on 1 to 1½ tons per foot of animal, a 30-footer has a lot of weight to throw around. Once the seal or penguin is thrown into the water, the show is soon over: one slashing bite and the Killer moves off, looking for new prey. Many an Antarctic explorer, in both past and recent times, has had the very disquieting experience of wandering close to the edge of the sea ice and suddenly finding himself staring into the eye of a Killer who had surfaced for a quick look around. Some of these encounters have been at distances of 2 and 3 feet.

An actual record of a very close scrape exists in Scott's journal of his last expedition. The date was January 5, 1911, and the entry reads, in part:

"I was a little late on the scene this morning, and thereby witnessed a most extraordinary scene. Some 6 or 7 Killer whales, old and young, were skirting the fast floe edge ahead of the ship; they seemed excited and dived rapidly, almost touching the floe. As we watched, they suddenly appeared astern, raising their snouts out of water. I had heard weird stories of these beasts but had never associated serious danger with them. Close to the water's edge lay the wire stern rope of the ship, and our two Esquimaux dogs were tethered to this. I did not think of connecting the movements of the whales with this fact, and seeing them so close, I shouted to Ponting, who was standing abreast of the ship. He seized his camera and ran towards the floe edge to get a close picture of the beasts, which had momentarily disappeared. The next moment the whole floe under him and the dogs heaved up and split into fragments. One could hear the 'booming' noise as the whales rose under the ice and struck it with their backs. Whale after whale rose under the ice, setting it rocking fiercely; luckily Ponting kept his feet and was able to fly to security. By an extraordinary chance, also, the splits had been made around and between the dogs, so that neither of them fell into the water. Then it was clear that the whales shared our astonishment, for one after another, their huge, hideous heads shot vertically into the air through the cracks which they had made. As they reared them to a height of 6 or 8 feet, it was possible to see their tawny head markings, their small glistening eyes, and their terrible array of teeth—by far the largest and most terrifying in the world. There cannot be a doubt that they looked up to see what had happened to Ponting and the dogs.

"The latter were horribly frightened and strained to their chains, whining; the head of one killer must certainly have been within 5 feet of one of the dogs . . .

"Of course, we have known well that Killer whales continually skirt the edge of the floes, and that they would undoubtedly snap up anyone who was unfortunate enough to fall into the water; but the facts that they could display such deliberate cunning, that they were able to break ice of such thickness (at least 2½ feet), and that they could act in unison, were a revelation to us. It is clear that they are endowed with singular intelligence with every respect."

Griffith Taylor, a member of Scott's last expedition, reported a somewhat similar encounter:

"We had noticed an unusual creaking sound, which I put down to ice crystals falling, but this strange object demanded investigation. I ran forward a little, and the black spike was obviously the back fin of a Killer whale. The creaking was really a warning that the bay ice was on the move. Meanwhile, the ice I was on moved with a jolt, a mark of attention from the Killer which we did not appreciate. However, I jumped the 3-foot crack which resulted, and we hastened to the fixed ice nearly 2 miles south."

There can't be any serious reason to doubt the word of either Captain Scott or Mr. Taylor. Both these men were trained scientific observers and could have no possible motive for cluttering up their personal journals with fabrications or exaggerations of any sort.

Endless stories have come down to us telling of whaleboats and other light craft, notably carrying seal-hunting crews, attacked and broken up by Killers. It is quite likely that this did occur, but we can't seem to verify it at the moment.

It is often stated that Killers have attempted to upset men into the water because they thought them to be seals or penguins. This may be true, but in trying to determine whether or not Killers are truly dangerous companions for man, it doesn't really matter. To a man who is about to vanish, in one or two pieces, down a gullet, it is pretty academic whether it is a case of mistaken identity or not.

My conclusion about the Killer whale is this: evidence is very incomplete and thoroughly shot through with the seagoing man's natural tendency to create a good yarn. The general rule that applies to just about any hunting animal applies to the Killer as well: if you look or act like his natural prey, you can get into serious difficulty. There is no way of knowing how often, or in what circumstances, a Killer would attack a man; and so, there is no way of predicting a safe encounter. Since there is no conceivable defense against these creatures, if you are in the water, the best rule would seem to be to stay out of the water and on thick ice that can't be tipped, when the presence of the Killer is suspected. They are carnivorous, with a special appetite for warm-blooded animals; and whether we like the idea or not, man is just more fresh meat in the eyes of some of nature's more aggressive species. The U.S. Navy advises its men that, although they have been unable to uncover an authentic account of a man being taken by a Killer, the creature is listed officially as a menace, and extreme caution is advised. Indeed, the Killer whale is the terror of the seas and the true villain of the Antarctic.

Whales are the source of many products valuable to man. Among these, the fine grades of oil, Grade "0" to Grade "4," are best known; but examine the following list, and you will soon see why the hunt goes on.

Products of Oil	Other Products
Additive in automatic transmission fluids	Whalemeat—excellent food
Textile chemicals	Whalemeat as a raw material for synthetic fibers
Plastics	
Cosmetics	Whalebone in brushes*
Detergents	Whalebone shavings for furniture stuffing
Jute processing	
Metallurgical operations	Ambergris,† perfume fixative
Leather dressing	Dried blood, excellent fertilizer
Fuel	Spermaceti,† wax for candles
Soap-making	Some whalehide, for leather
Precision-machinery lubricants‡	General waste, after oil extraction, used as protein feed for hogs, cattle, poultry, dogs, fur animals, and in fertilizer
Cooking fats	
Paint and varnish	
Printing ink	Vitamin A from liver
Lard compounds	Pharmaceutical material from organs
Cooking oils	Glue
Wool oiling	Machinery belts
Flax batching	Shoelaces
Preserving grease	
Oilcloth and linoleum manufacture	
Glycerin	

‡ Sperm and Bottlenose whale only.

* Nowhere near as valuable as it once was, when it was used in leaf springs, as corset stays, and a dozen other commodities.

† From the Sperm whale only.

A Norwegian by the name of Svend Foyn invented the explosive harpoon during the last century, and with its appearance, whaling assumed production-line proportions. The days when men faced their monster prey in open boats and approached close enough for the harpooner to sink his shaft by hand rapidly died out, taking with it one of the most romantic of man's professions. The immediate result was, and is, serious over-whaling. There are innumerable treaties, agreements, understandings, and conferences, but still many whale species are pushed toward extinction. Whales reproduce slowly, certainly not more than once every two years. In April, 1961, the National Academy of Sciences stated that a known total of 1,027,332 whales have been taken in Antarctic waters in the past 50 years. Dr. Remington Kellogg, Assistant Secretary of the Smithsonian Institution, said that there is little doubt that, at the present rate of slaughter, whales are being killed faster than they can reproduce themselves. Conferences form and break up in disagreement or set bag limits that are promptly ignored. The situation is going from bad to worse.

As we have pointed out, the whale is a pretty bright animal. In recent years, many cases have been reported where pods of whales have adopted wartime convoy tactics to avoid slaughter. They scatter when attacked, something quite contrary to their normal herd behavior. The whales execute sharp turns and sometimes come astern of the chaser. There is every evidence that whales are passing on new evasive tactics to succeeding generations.

As impressive as this display of intelligence and adaptability is, we can readily predict that the whale will not be able to keep up with modern whaling improvements. Sonar, radar, and helicopters are just three of the new instruments now in use by whalers. If it was sad to see the Passenger pigeon vanish from America, and the Great Auk from northern Atlantic islands, how infinitely more sad it will be to see the giant of all giants disappear from the world's seas. But, that is exactly what is happening. Unless something really significant is done, and done *soon*, the mighty whale will not only become ancient history in Antarctica, but throughout the rest of the world as well. It will probably not be possible for man to kill all the whales in the world. The oceans are far too vast and the whale far too clever. What will happen is that the whale will diminish in numbers and increase in evasive intelligence to the point where it will cease to be of economic importance. The sighting of a whale will be as much an occasion as the report of a wolf or a mountain lion seen in New England. Whales were once seen regularly and in great numbers in the waterways around New York. Indians hunted them in Long Island Sound. Today, a whale in that body of water creates a carnival atmosphere, as sightseers come to stare at what will probably be the only whale they will ever see during their life. This author has had the good fortune to see whales on a number of occasions: off the Hawaiian Islands, south of New Zealand, off the coast of New Hampshire, in the Bay of Fundy, and, perhaps, in one or two other places. It is a magnificent sight, and I should hate to think that future generations may miss it entirely.

THE SEALS

The Seals, or *Pinnipedia*, represent the only group of mammals, other than whales, that exist in the Antarctic. This group has only a few regular southern species; the Crabeater (*Lobodon carcino-*

phagus), the Weddell (*Leptonychotes weddelli*), the Ross (*Ommatophoca rossi*), and the Leopard seal (*Hydrurga leptonyx*). A fifth, the Elephant seal (*Mirounga leonina*), is found only occasionally. It is one of two seals of the far South having economic value. It yields an important oil. The fur seal (*Arctocephalus* sp.) which, along with the whale, first attracted the serious attention of the world to Antarctic wastes, had for years been believed to be extinct. A few small herds have recently been seen, and their number is increasing. It is to be hoped that man will be a little wiser, now that he has a second chance, and not drive this interesting and valuable animal beyond the point of no return.

The diets of the Antarctic seals are simple and easy to describe. The Crabeater shares the baleen whale's taste for red krill, while the others live mostly on fish. The notable exception, as we shall see, is the Leopard seal, the second villain of the southern seas.

It is interesting to note the estimated seal population. Victor B. Scheffer, in his *Seals, Sea Lions, and Walruses*, published by the Stanford University Press in 1958, gives these estimated figures:

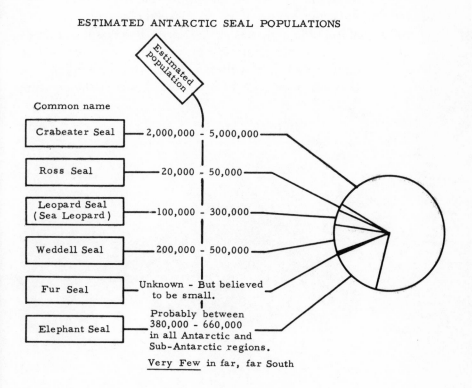

ESTIMATED ANTARCTIC SEAL POPULATIONS

Estimated population

Common name	
Crabeater Seal	2,000,000 - 5,000,000
Ross Seal	20,000 - 50,000
Leopard Seal (Sea Leopard)	100,000 - 300,000
Weddell Seal	200,000 - 500,000
Fur Seal	Unknown - But believed to be small.
Elephant Seal	Probably between 380,000 - 660,000 in all Antarctic and Sub-Antarctic regions. Very Few in far, far South

The whales are the only mammals more completely adapted to life in the sea than the pinnipeds. The seals are nearly as well adapted as the great cetaceans and have the added advantage of being able to survive out of water. Whales can't survive out of water because of their great weight. Without the cushioning effect of the marine environment, whales would suffocate. Even their great muscles couldn't push their enormous bulk up enough to allow their lungs to fill. Seals have no such problem, although they are not exactly gazelle-like when high and dry.

All seals must return to dry land or ice to give birth, and all of them retreat out of the water when Killer whales are on the prowl. The only enemy the seal has, besides the Killer whales and man, is the Sea-leopard, a large solitary devil weighing as much as 1,200 pounds and growing to a length of 10 or 12 feet. The Sea-leopard, or Leopard seal, probably does most of his killing in the water; so from this predator, too, the smaller seals of the Antarctic take refuge on rock and ice.

There are, of course, no polar bears outside of the Arctic regions —nothing comparable at all in the south—and man hasn't been around the Antarctic long enough to make the seal wary, as his relationship with the Eskimo has in the North. The delightful result is that Antarctic seals are unafraid, once out of the water. It is a strange sensation to walk up to within a foot of a totally wild animal, possibly one that has never seen a man before, and have the creature

The face of a curious Weddell Seal.

Bull Sea-elephants fighting.

stare you right in the eye. He will not attempt to escape, although his ice hole may be only inches away; and he will generally exhibit no aggressive action, except to show you his teeth half-heartedly for a moment. If you stand around long enough, he will turn his head away and go to sleep.

Seals differ considerably in size. The following table gives the average sizes encountered for each species. It must be kept in mind that the Antarctic is a large place, large enough, certainly, to encourage and support the development of subspecies and races. A seal that inhabits the coastal region of Antarctica due south of New Zealand may not be the same size as a seal of the same species found due south of Africa or South America. The study is far from complete but, setting aside regional differences and individual peculiarities, fair averages are shown in the accompanying table.

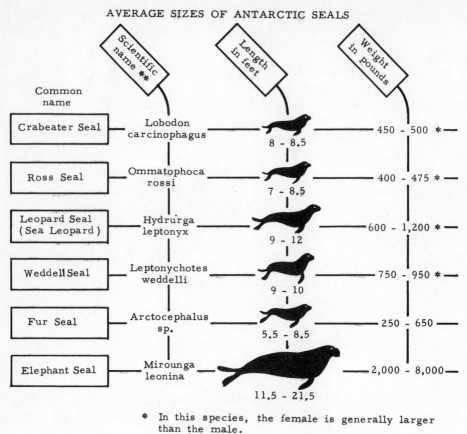

Common name	Scientific name **	Length in feet		Weight in pounds
Crabeater Seal	Lobodon carcinophagus	8 - 8.5		450 - 500 *
Ross Seal	Ommatophoca rossi	7 - 8.5		400 - 475 *
Leopard Seal (Sea Leopard)	Hydrurga leptonyx	9 - 12		600 - 1,200 *
Weddell Seal	Leptonychotes weddelli	9 - 10		750 - 950 *
Fur Seal	Arctocephalus sp.	5.5 - 8.5		250 - 650
Elephant Seal	Mirounga leonina	11.5 - 21.5		2,000 - 8,000

* In this species, the female is generally larger than the male.

** Note that no two of the six Antarctic Seals belong to the same genus: — The first name being the genus, the second the species.

The Elephant seal is the largest of all the pinnipeds, outranking even the huge walrus of the North by a respectable margin. There are a number of races of the Elephant seal, but all are still listed as the same species. The different races or regional groups center around the Falkland Islands in the South Atlantic, the Macquarie Islands southeast of Tasmania, Heard Island in the South Indian Ocean, off the coast of Baja California, and several other south oceanic areas. A first cousin, but of a different species, is found in northern waters. It isn't quite clear which of these races is found most commonly all the way south on the coast of Antarctica.

The prancing, barking Sea lion of the circus is a misleading example of the pinnipeds. The seals of Antarctica can neither play "God Bless America" on a series of tin trumpets nor balance striped balls on their noses. On the ice or rocky coast, they are sluggish and quite dull. Their torpedo-shaped body is enveloped in thick sub-cutaneous fat. In the Weddell seal, more than 25 per cent of the animal's hulk consists of this blubbery layer between fur and muscle. This blubber has many functions. It protects the animal against the cold (both air and water); it provides reserve energy during long fasts and while females are nursing their pups; it provides buoyancy in the water, since fat is lighter than water; and it provides the padding necessary to fill out and complete the streamlined shape.

Blubber alone would not be enough protection from the cold. The seal has a high rate of metabolism and consumes large quanti-ties of food. Part of this food goes to serve the animal's immediate needs and part goes to keep up the blubber storage level. Seals often take fish far larger than they can gulp down, and since they have no means of holding their prey while they tear it apart, they shake it apart. They have immensely strong necks to aid them in this proce-dure.

In the water, seals are very fast. It is quite certain that most of them, the Elephant seal being a probable exception, can travel be-tween 10 and 15 miles an hour when inspired to do so by a Killer whale or in pursuit of food. They are good jumpers and have been seen to jump 8 to 10 feet out of the water, to splash back in 20 feet away.

On land, seals don't generally do as well. They drive back in powerful strokes with their front flippers and take powerful thrusts from their hind flippers. The Antarctic Crabeater seal is, quite pos-sibly, the fastest pinniped on land. Reportedly, a Crabeater can

New Zealand Trans-Antarctic Expedition

Weddell Seal and 2-day-old pup.

101

reach 15 to 16 miles an hour—for short sprints. At normal land speed, a seal would probably do only twice that distance in a whole day. Seals are made for the world of water.

The Leopard seal is the second largest pinniped found in the Antarctic and, as we have pointed out, the second villain. He is in no way as formidable a villain as number one, the Killer whale, but he seems to have had some success at building up a reputation for himself. There can be little doubt that 12 feet and 1,200 pounds of angry seal is a lot to contend with, and the legend-makers of the Antarctic have had some pretty good tales to tell. Naturally, we hear that they are dangerous to man. In his account of his first expedition, "The Voyage of the '*Discovery*,'" published in 1905, Captain Scott speaks of one opening his "formidable jaws" and threatening the explorers "in the most ferocious manner." In his account of his 1907–1909 expedition, *The Heart of the Antarctic—1909*, Ernest Shackleton commented that "the Sea-leopards are savage and aggressive, and can move very rapidly on the ice." He tells of the obtaining of a specimen for the biologists to study. After being shot twice through the heart and twice through the skull with a "heavy revolver," the beast continued to struggle. A fifth bullet in the brain still didn't kill it outright, and it kept up the fight for several minutes. There can be little doubt that they could be a formidable foe to deal with if you got caught at close quarters by a specimen inclined to attack.

Most seals are very social animals, and a colony may range in size from a dozen to close to a million, at least during the breeding sea-

New Zealand Trans-Antarctic Expedition

Weddell Seal swimming at the edge of the ice.

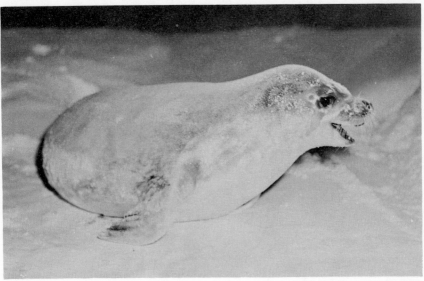

A rare picture of a Crab Eating Seal.

son. The Sea-leopard, like the Ross seal, tends to be solitary, and seldom are more than a few encountered in a general area. More likely than not, on the ice, even finding a few close together is accidental—a chance meeting. It is only during the summer months that they are found on the coasts and the coastal ice of the Antarctic. They head north to breed, and the stories of their ferocity come from both ends of their range. Although I have been unable to find a verified account of a Sea-leopard actually assaulting a man, there are stories designed, no doubt, to tingle the fancy of the uninitiated. Tales of poor, weary explorers stumbling and skidding across the ice with a half-a-ton of angry, hungry Leopard seal snapping at their heels, are often heard. It is generally implied that they look on man as a good meal. Once again, we are forced to admit that this could be possible. The Leopard seal usually dines on penguins (the 3-foot Emperor included), and other seals as well as fish, and could certainly do a man in if he caught him. When angry, the Leopard seal does snap viciously while whirling in place and thrusting his snaky head and neck forward. His obviously miserable disposition, his great size and ferocious teeth, when coupled with his habit of snapping, seem to have combined to create the legend of their assaults on man. We repeat, it isn't impossible—we just don't know of it happening. Almost any seal, molested, can be dangerous at close quarters. The teeth are designed for grasping, as a rule, and the jaws are powerful.

103

A starved, young male Leopard Seal found on the Ross Ice Shelf.

In taking the legends of any remote area and comparing them with the facts, once they have been established, you could almost draw a graph. The more remote the area, the greater the spread between fact and fiction. I contend that it is less a case of lack of information than a case of obligation! It is an obligation, assumed by the few who go far, to live up to the expectations of the many who stay home. I certainly don't contend that all world travelers are, or were in the old days, liars. I do maintain that the temptation is great, and always has been, to fulfill the role of conquering hero or, at least, returning world traveler.

Put yourself in the place of a man returning from the Antarctic some years ago. After the hugging and the kissing and the distributing of gifts, the whole clan gathers around, and a sea of upturned and intent faces waits for the stories to start. You, the traveling man, look around and see the collection of kinfolk and neighbors, most of whom never went farther than a hundred miles from home. Sitting across from you is an old school chum who became a clerk in a dry-goods store while you set out into the teeth of the wind. What are

New Zealand Trans-Antarctic Expedition

An Antarctic seal clambers out of his ice hole.

you to do? Can you just shrug and say it was cold and windy, and
that bruises from slipping on the ice were a common complaint?
Hardly! You owe it to friends and neighbors to do better than that.
And so it is, that people bob up and down the whale's gullet and
fight duels with Sea-leopards. It is a natural outgrowth of man's in-
nate sense of drama and a very honest kind of prevarication. The
only trouble is, these storytelling bees somehow survive in our
lore and ripen in time. If *two* "old explorers" get set up at the
same session, then competition increases not only the tempo of
the stories, but their length, breadth, and height as well. Stories of
the most ridiculous kind have persisted, despite logic and education.
Milk snakes still milk cows, hoop snakes still take tail in mouth and
roll down hills, and Sea-leopards still take gastronomic delight in
filet of explorer. An additional problem exists in the fact that many
tales of Antarctic mammals have an element of plausibilty. While you
can easily prove that it is absolutely impossible for a milk snake
to milk a cow, you can't prove that it is impossible for the Sea-
leopard and the Killer whale to do *most* of the things of which they

105

The breathing hole.

are accused. It only remains to discover if they ever really do them. Perhaps we will find some of these answers, now that the human population of the Antarctic has increased from dozens to hundreds.

Not all the strange tales told by returning whalers and sealers were fiction. There are many unsolved mysteries connected with animal behavior in the Antarctic, as everywhere else in the world. Not the least of these is "the mystery of the mixed-up seals."

Seals, with the exception of a few lake-dwellers, live at and belong to the edge of the sea. Only during migrations from breeding to feeding grounds are they encountered in the open sea. This author recalls, as one of the great thrills of his life, the sight of a seal migration in the Pacific. For nearly two hours, the sea in every direction, as far as the eye could see, throbbed with the undulating bodies of what must have been hundreds of thousands of seals, en route north to breeding grounds just below the Arctic Circle. It is not a sight one is likely to forget.

With the exception of these open-water journeys, when they are preyed upon by sharks, the seals are restricted to the edge of the sea by their very way of life. They live off the sea, being unequipped to hunt or forage on land. This is particularly true in the Antarctic, where there is nothing on land to eat. The possible exception would be the Sea-leopard, who conceivably might take a seal pup or penguin on the ice, but even this is doubtful. Seals are so much better equipped to maneuver in water than on a solid surface.

Almost every seal, walrus, and sea lion in the world can be found within feet or yards of the ocean. Rocky coasts of continents, edges of ice shelves, small islets, sand bars—these are the haunts of most seals. Most, we say, because a few (and we don't know how many) go astray, contrary to all sense and logic. These mixed-up wanderers are a mystery to science.

The *New York Times,* on September 24, 1959, carried an account of this mystery by Walter Sullivan, one of America's finest writers on science subjects. The article says that wanderlust may be at the root of this mystery. The mystery is this—why should seals, totally acclimated to life in the sea and in great danger of starvation when away from it, suddenly decide on an inland journey? That is exactly what has happened, not once, but many times.

Seals, singly and in large groups, have been found between 30 and 40 miles inland. New Zealanders, on one expedition alone, found 99 dead seals as far as 35 miles from the ocean. Two scientists of the U.S. Geological Survey and one from the National Academy of Sciences, did a study on 90 more of these animals that had committed suicide by striking out across country. Some of these 90 were found 30 miles inland and *at an elevation of 3,000 feet!*

A seal in water is at ease; a seal on ice is able to get around quite well; but a seal on a rocky slope, on any kind of bare upgrade, can move only with the greatest imaginable difficulty. Seals are totally unequipped for mountain climbing or for negotiating any craggy area. The retreating glaciers we will be dealing with in another chapter have left ice-free valleys in a number of regions in Antarctica. Seals have been found in these rock-filled valleys, dead, apparently from starvation, many miles from any water or possible source of food.

The Lamont Geological Observatory dated one carcass by measuring the radioactive carbon content and found that it was between 1,600 and 2,600 years old. Since things don't rot in the Antarctic, it is not surprising that the animal was found intact. What is surprising is that the animal was found 1,640 feet above where it belonged —sea level.

There are a number of explanations that have been put forward. The suggestion that they were "lost" doesn't seem very logical. Seals migrate hundreds and frequently thousands of miles, and somehow it is difficult to understand their wandering away from the water and getting lost. The direction-finding ability of migrating animals is one of the miracles of nature. Even those Antarctic seals that don't really migrate to distant lands head to the open sea and float-

University of Texas scientist examining a mummified Crab Eating Seal.

ing ice when winter locks the continent in for half the year. Simply getting lost doesn't seem to be the answer.

A rather more dramatic theory has the seals reverting to ancestral behavior. The seals, like the whales, are descended from land animals; and this theory has it that a sudden change comes over these animals that makes them forget what they are and remember what they were long, long ago, in the dim past. There is something inherently exciting about this idea, but it leaves a number of questions unanswered. What triggers this freak behavior? What suddenly makes this happen? Why do groups suddenly succumb to this fatal memory? Why do others escape it? We can't eliminate this theory any more than we can any others, but it certainly needs further clarification.

A great many of the seals found dead of wanderlust were Crabeaters. These seals are unable to chew holes through ice, as other species can; so, if caught by a sudden freeze, they are isolated from water and food. Could these seals have been caught this way and, in the desperation of near starvation, struck out in the wrong direction? This theory has been proposed, but it, too, leaves unanswered questions. Not *all* seals found high and dry were Crabeaters. Why should Leopard seals and Weddells behave this way?

Why would any seals, even very hungry ones, suddenly lose their great directional finding systems? Why inland, instead of toward open water and life?

Most of the seals found far inland apparently died of starvation. Very little blubber was left on their bodies, and their stomachs were empty. Was this sad situation the result of their mad journey away from life, or the cause of it? A little farther on, we will be listing some of the mysteries, the unanswered questions, of the Antarctic. This one, however, is as perplexing as any. Maybe the answer will be found when more of the Antarctic has been explored. Thousands of square miles of the coastal region are unknown. Perhaps, when man finally reaches these untouched, unseen regions, the riddle may be solved. Could the seals be looking for something we don't even know exists? Who knows!

We must conclude our chapter on mammals by acknowledging two other points. First, no fossils have been found that would indicate that any land mammals ever existed on the Southern Continent. The mammals there now, those from the sea, are probably all that ever existed. Throughout the history of life on Earth, nature has been evolving strange and wonderful land creatures—everywhere on our planet, except on its fifth largest continent.

The second and last point in this chapter is a list of the other mammal species that have lived in this ice-age land:

Homo sapiens	man	*Canis familiaris*	dog
Felis cattus	cat, alley	*Equus caballus*	pony

All arrived within the last hundred years, and all are visitors only.

When the author visited the South Pole Station, he noted that a big old tom housecat, kept there as a pet, had grown a coat of fur of great density. It was thicker, by far, than any he had seen on a cat before. Nature, apparently, has remarkable reserves for those who can't help themselves. The South Pole cat had a look of constant bewilderment on his face, and one can't help but wonder if he knew how far he was from his nearest relative.

Interestingly enough, the Antarctic is probably one of extremely few areas in the world where ships have called and the rat hasn't taken hold. Even this, one of the most adaptable creatures on earth, hasn't been able to get a toe-hold.

In all of history, man and his pets are probably the only land mammals the Antarctic has ever known, although, as mentioned earlier, the ice holds many secrets.

7

Penguins, Plants, and Plankton

Not all life native to the Antarctic is as ponderously impressive as the whale or as strangely enigmatic as the seal. The universal animal symbol of the Southern Continent wears feathers and is possessed of what must be described as a sense of humor. At once stately and comical, the penguin is a cartoon character come to life.

THE FLIGHTLESS BIRDS

Flight, the most immediately recognizable characteristic of bird life, is not something of which all birds are capable. Quite plainly, not everything that flies is a bird and not every bird can fly.

Flightless birds have developed over much of the world under widely differing conditions. The one factor common to all of the relationships between these birds and their environments was that it was not important for the birds to fly. Once flight has ceased to be a life necessity, the bird has taken the first major step toward losing the ability to free itself of the ground. It may never actually become flightless, but all those which have, went through this first step—freedom from necessity.

Flightless birds include the ostrich (*Struthio camelus*) on the open plains of Africa; the rheas (*Rhea* and *Pterocnemia*) in a similar environment in South America; the emu (*Dromiceius*) and the cassowary (*Casuarius*) in Australia and New Guinea; the kiwi (*Apteryx*), the kakapo parrot (*Strigops*), and the takahe (*Notornis*) in New Zealand; and the penguin (*Sphenisciformes*) throughout the Southern hemisphere. There are others we haven't mentioned, not only extant but extinct. Among the more interesting flightless birds that failed to survive a changing world are the flightless goose (*Anseres*) and swan of New Zealand; the moas (*Dinornithidae*), the dodo (*Raphus*), and the solitaire (*Pezophaps*) of the Indian Ocean islands; and the Great Auk (*Pinguinis*) of the coasts, rocks, and skerries of the North Atlantic.

In each case, the flightless bird was either big enough or isolated enough, during the period of its development, to be relatively free of danger while on the ground. Man, in most cases, brought an end to the danger-free life of these interesting animals. Where he didn't limit the bird's range and safety himself, he caused its decline by importing, either accidentally or on purpose, enemies with which the bird could not cope. Pigs, dogs, cats, and rats all have either hunted the birds or their eggs and brought about extinction or near-extinction.

In the North, man himself wiped out the Great Auk. In New Zealand, it has long been believed, he did the same to the various moas —one of them being the largest bird that ever lived, achieving an estimated height of eleven or twelve feet. In certain remote regions, New Zealand's flightless takahe and kakapo have both been recently rediscovered, after having been listed as extinct for at least a century; and there is now reason to believe that even the moa continues to exist, albeit in smaller forms, in some forgotten valley. The one flightless group that seems to have fared the best (besides the ostriches, rheas, cassowaries, and emus) is the penguin tribe. Although some forms have vanished and others have been reduced to small colonies, the penguins, as a whole, continue to thrive in their unique way of life.

In all the vast expanse of the Southern Hemisphere, there is only one family of penguins. This is divided into either 14 or 15 species, depending on which authority you want to accept. In numbers, penguins exist in the many millions. A single Antarctic breeding colony, or rookery, can contain a million or more birds. This delightful creature has learned to survive the storm of man's arrival, just as he has survived the storms of Antarctic weather extremes. He seems to be in little danger at the moment, as a group. Today, he is found on those coasts of Africa and South America that extend below the equator, in Australia and New Zealand, in the islands of the Atlantic, Pacific, and Indian oceans, and in the Antarctic itself.

Although the penguin has been an inhabitant of the South since time immemorial, his name has been there only for the last century and a half. "Penguin" may come from two Welsh words meaning either "white head" or "fat bird," actually applied to the Great Auk of the North—a bird somewhat similar, but unrelated, which now is believed to be extinct. The Great Auk was hunted for its feathers, its edible flesh, and its valuable oil. In June of 1844, two men, Jon Brandsson and Ketil Ketilsson, each killed a Great Auk on a rocky islet, or skerry, off Iceland, called Eldey. No authenticated record of a living Great Auk is known from that time on. Peter Matthiessen, in his excellent book, *Wildlife in America* (Viking Press, 1959), gives a dramatic account of the incident.

Seamen, ranging the oceans of the world in pursuit of the whale and the Fur seal, brought the name "penguin" south and applied it to flightless birds they encountered there, and the name stuck.

Antarctica has only 2 of the 14 or 15 known species of penguin —the very common Adelie (*Pygoscelis adeliae*) and the relatively more rare Emperor. The Emperor (*Aptenoides forsteri*) is the largest of the living penguins and actually achieves a height of between 3 and 4 feet. Fossils uncovered in New Zealand and the South Orkneys prove that penguins once existed that were the height of a full-grown man!

Penguins are an ancient tribe, probably developing as we know them today between 50 and 100 million years ago. They almost certainly emerged from birds that could fly, judging from the fact that they have a keel bone in their chest and wing quills during their embryonic life. The peculiar structure of their beak, a group of horny plates and not a single sheath, may point to descent from a kind of albatross. Other features can point to a relationship with the loons, cormorants, and pelicans. Interestingly, all of the characteristics of penguin life and structure point to probable or possible kinship with birds of the world of water. No bird, now alive or ever existing, could be better adapted to life in the sea. The penguin is as truly a marine creature as the seal or the whale, some of which it can even out-perform.

We have said that penguins can't fly. If we use the word "fly" to mean "to move in or pass through the air," admittedly the best meaning of the word according to Webster, then it is true. If we take a somewhat broader view of the word (also in Webster) "to

Emperor Penguins arrive at the U.S. Navy installation at McMurdo Sound.

move or pass swiftly," then penguins can fly with superb skill, for the penguin literally flies through the water. Its flippers, vestiges of its once powerful wings, are the means by which it flies in the sea. It uses its flippers in the water just as other birds use their wings in the sky, and penguins can achieve a speed of at least twenty-five miles an hour once submerged. Allowing for the fact that the marine environment is considerably more dense than the world of air currents, the use of the flipper is much like that of the wing.

A penguin is best suited to life under the water, and it is there that it feeds. Captive penguins have to be taught forcibly how to eat above water, all their instincts being to do so beneath the surface. Once free of a hard surface, penguins move like darts. They shoot through the submarine world with infinite skill, changing course without effort. Their powerful flippers give them the propelling force; their heavy webbed feet, mounted on chunky legs, are their rudders; their feathers, close-packed and uniformly thick over all their torpedo-like bodies, are completely impervious to water; and their layers of blubber give them a perfect neutral buoyancy, in balance with their denser body weight. It is difficult to imagine an animal better suited to life in the sea.

Penguins often swim in packs, like porpoises, and move along

Official U.S. Navy Photograph

Adelie Penguin and egg—Cape Royds, Ross Island.

at great speed beneath the surface, arcing up through the waves only to breathe. When they decide to "land" on an ice cake bobbing overhead, they shoot up through the water and, after passing through the surface continue up 6 feet or more, landing upright on the ice. If they miss and slip back into the water, they try and try again. The bobbing up and down of these birds is indeed a comical sight. Since the last flipper motion they make before cracking through the surface is a downward thrust, they emerge stiff and streamlined, "arms" at their sides, for all the world like a clown on a trampoline. A certain urgency is added to this maneuver when Killer whales

114

Emperor Penguin and chick.

or Leopard seals are about, since these villains take a delight in the flesh of the penguin and are its principal enemies.

Penguins feed on fish, shrimp, and squid and return to ice or land to breed, to raise their young, to hide from enemies, and to play. They have several ways of getting around once out of the water; waddle, hop, and skim. Upright, they either hop along, feet close together like a youngster in a potato sack race, or waddle along rocking from foot to foot and looking not just a little bit drunk. When in a hurry, they flop onto their stomachs and really dig in with their flippers. Skimming along on their bellies, they can

Official U.S. Navy Photograph
Emperors and USS GLACIER.

leave a man on skis well behind. On downgrades, the penguin lets himself go and is a perfect self-contained toboggan. His powerful, thick legs act like pistons, giving him added thrust.

On the ice, Antarctic penguins have one other enemy—the skua (*Catharacta skua*). This gull-like bird feeds, to some extent, on penguin eggs and chicks. Certain petrels, and perhaps one or two other migratory sea birds, may also prey on eggs and chicks to a limited degree. The skua is probably the only real enemy the penguin has out of the water, and even from this mighty bird, the adult penguin is safe. We will come to the skua in turn.

Man was once a penguin enemy, but the period when this was true was too brief either to endanger the penguin's existence or to teach the bird to fear man. Whaling ships and sealers, when running short of fuel, would come ashore and club the fearless, gregarious birds to death by the thousands. Their fat-rich bodies make an excellent fuel. Their oil, when rendered from the blubber, burns even better than mammal oil. Their flesh is edible but, I am told, not exactly New England turkey. The sea food on which the penguin thrives permeates its own flesh, giving it an oily, fishy taste that makes it, really, only emergency fare. Many men get sick from it.

Today, man is careful of the penguin. Antarctic groups avoid harming the birds or upsetting their breeding colonies as much as

116

possible. Captain Finn Ronne, during the IGY, set an excellent example of how to discourage depredations of this delightful, harmless bird. Any of his men who wanted to take a penguin as a souvenir of his tour of duty on the ice had to deposit $50.00 with his Commanding Officer and then kill his bird in a prescribed manner. Once the man had returned to civilization, he had to obtain a certificate from a professional taxidermist saying that the bird had been mounted, within a specified time, or sacrifice the $50.00. This discouraged thoughtless members of the expedition from "hunting" penguins just to pass the time. Compared with penguins, sitting ducks are sporting game. All you have to do to kill a penguin is walk up to it and knock it on the head. A more senseless slaughter cannot be imagined. It is discouraged and seldom practiced today, except to acquire scientific specimens.

We have said that the penguin is unafraid of man. As a matter of fact, he is fascinated by this two-legged creature from distant lands. Penguins can be a terrible nuisance because they are often so delighted with man's apparently funny behavior that they get under foot. Some scientific stations have had to set up fences to keep penguins out during construction. The birds were constantly getting in the way, and work was delayed by the efforts of the men not to hurt them. The fences seldom did much good, and penguins still mingled with the men, without regard for potential danger.

This author never ceases to be amazed at the behavior of some

Chief Leo Loftus and a totally unconcerned Emperor chick.

117

of his fellow men, when it comes to animals. During my visit to the Antarctic, I was privileged to hitch a ride with a few other observers on a helicopter going to the Adelie penguin rookery at Cape Royds on Ross Island. It was spring (November), and the breeding season was on in full. Royds is a relatively small rookery, as penguin breeding colonies go, and about 19,000 of the 30-inch-high Adelies were setting up housekeeping, choosing mates, and admiring newly laid eggs. Nearby is the hut Shackleton built nearly half a century ago, and in it lived two New Zealanders who were doing a study of the colony. A professor from Canterbury College, who headed the study project, was guiding us through the remarkable area, telling us of the penguins' habits. Suddenly, one of our little group, a correspondent from a leading European newspaper, went off on his own and began running back and forth among the newly formed penguin families. Shouting, and waving his arms like a madman, he frightened females off their nests and broke up love-making rituals. He came back, out of breath and chuckling to himself like someone who had taken leave of his senses. The professor from New Zealand, who had spent so much time studying these interesting birds and had taken such pains to do so without upsetting their normal routine, muttered something about how pleased he would be to have a gun at hand. The rest of us grunted in assent, and we went on our way, watching and learning about these strange ice-age creatures. As strange as any animal may be, he is outdone by man, at least some men, in weird and unfathomable behavior.

The two Antarctic penguins are quite different in breeding habits. The Adelie, far and away the more common of the two, breeds in the early spring, arriving at the rookery in late October and early November. These rookeries are often some miles away from water, and there is a period of fasting for the adults, until the young have been hatched. When they first arrive, the females stand around, waiting for the males to take the initiative. The male does this by finding a pebble and bringing it to a female he finds particularly to his liking. He lays the pebble at her feet and stands around, expectantly waiting for her to make a decision. If she pushes the pebble around a little with her beak, he has a chance; and if she picks it up after examining it, he has himself a wife. The newly betrothed couple stand close together, often belly to belly, and sing a love duet. A rookery, at this time of the year, is a very active and noisy place.

That penguins, at least the busy little Adelie penguins, are criminal by nature cannot be doubted. While the newly formed pair

A crowd of Emperors and chicks at Cape Crozier.

are crooning of their future life together, more likely than not, an unattached male will attempt to steal the pebble. He needs it to win himself a wife and is not the least bit concerned with the fact that it no longer belongs to the rival male, but is the proud possession of the bride. He is very likely to get caught in the act, and the other male will stop his love song long enough to dash after the villain and administer a mighty beating with his flippers. The fight can get quite vicious, and blood may be drawn. The flipper is hard and can deliver a powerful blow. In the Emperor penguin, the blow of a flipper could break a man's arm.

While the battle rages up and down through the rookery, the other birds will cheer the hero on, voicing their utter disgust with criminal behavior. Some of the loud onlookers will stop in their efforts to steal pebbles themselves, to join the chorus. Once the fight is over and they have had their say about criminals who steal pebbles, they go about their business, trying to steal some. Pebbles are a status symbol, obviously, and from them a crude kind of nest is made.

Penguins return year after year to the same rookery which is inevitably, in the case of the Adelie, an area where the snow melts enough to expose bare ground and the all-important pebbles.

The *New York Times,* on December 3, 1960, carried a fascinating account of an experiment that proves just how fussy the Adelie penguin is about his rookery. In 1959, Richard Lee Penney, a University of Wisconsin zoologist, banded five Adelies at Wilkes Station, 1,500 air miles from McMurdo Sound. The five birds were then flown across the continent to McMurdo Sound and set loose. In early November, 1960, two of the birds showed up at Wilkes a few days apart. Since they didn't arrive together, it can be surmised that they traveled alone. A third bird showed up without a band, but with indications that it had once been banded. These birds could not possibly have gone across the continent and so must have gone around. It is estimated that they traveled between 2,250 and 2,400 statute miles—covering 60 degrees of longitude. These birds must have passed tens of thousands of other Adelies, in their monumental trek, and dozens of possible nesting sites; yet they continued on to their own native rookery. The mystery of the "how" of this episode is equalled by the mystery of the "why." Why should the home rookery hold such a magnetic power over these birds? Why wouldn't other colonies of the same species do as well? And, how do they find their way over such vast distances? Even the laughable, lovable penguin has great hidden depths that deserve careful probing. Just imagine what it would be like if the secret of the penguins' direction-finding system could be interpreted, and the art transferred to man!

The stately Emperor penguin has a breeding cycle quite the opposite of the Adelie. Strangely, the Emperor breeds in the bitter dark of mid-winter, and a great deal less is known about the event. Pebbles, obviously, are not involved, and no nest is attempted. Quite probably, the Emperor is the only bird who never sets foot on dry, bare land. He is born on the frozen wastes in winter and spends his summer, it is assumed, on floating ice.

The Emperors stand around in a circle, keeping the young in the middle as protection against the wind and driving snow. The egg is kept on top of the feet, tucked up into folds of fat in the belly. It is constantly turned over to keep the warmth of the parent's body evenly distributed. After the young are born, they will frequently hitch a ride by climbing aboard the parent's feet.

Penguins are doting parents, and many chicks die from too much love. Mature penguins are so eager to adopt every chick they see, that many presumed strays are killed by parents and would-be

120

The growth of an Adelie Penguin.

Emperor chicks hiding from the world.

foster parents fighting over them. The large rookeries, apparently, have an educational system; and a common sight is a few adults with a whole swarm of chicks, off on a fishing or swimming lesson. It is obvious that they are tutors of sorts, and the education of the young is a definite program, assigned to certain mature birds.

Penguins are not very bright animals. They respond to well-developed instincts and behave within very predictable patterns. Clever or not, these symbols of Antarctica, the regal and impressive Emperor penguin and the clownlike little Adelie, are a fascinating study. Fortunately for man, there are a lot of secrets concerning these birds left to uncover, a lot of fascinating detective work to be done.

THE OTHER BIRDS OF ANTARCTICA

Besides the two penguins, there are a number of other birds often seen over Antarctic waters and along the continent's ice-locked coast. With one exception, these birds are summer visitors only. One visitor is truly extraordinary—the Arctic tern (*Sterna paradi-*

saea.). This most ambitious of all sun-worshippers nests in the Canadian Arctic during summer in the Northern hemisphere and leaves for the South as soon as winter issues its first warning. Weeks later, the Arctic tern appears in the Antarctic, 11,000 miles away, for the southern summer. At the end of the Antarctic summer, this great traveler turns around and heads back across one-half the world. The only dark hours this bird experiences occur during its two annual migrations. It spends the rest of the time in the eternal light of the polar regions' summer months.

There are some 30 species of birds seen regularly near the southern continent. They are fulmars (*Fulmarimae*), petrels (*Procellarii formes*), terns (*Sterninae*), and other water-birds. Every bird that is associated with Antarctica is automatically tied to the sea. Not only is the ocean its migratory route, but it is also the only source for its food. The Antarctic continent offers poor pickings, even for short-term visitors. The Giant Fulmar (*Macronectes giganteus*), the Silver-gray Fulmar (*Fulmarus glacialoides*), the handsome Snowy petrel (*Pagodroma nivea*), and the Cape pigeon (*Daption capense*) are a few regularly reported summer tourists. Like man and the whales, many birds await the Antarctic summer before turning south for the few months of sun only then available.

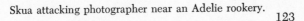

Official U.S. Navy Photograph

Skua attacking photographer near an Adelie rookery.

Skua and chick and close-up of newly hatched chicks.

The exception we referred to, the only truly Antarctic bird with the power of flight, is the skua—a close relative of the gulls, which they strongly resemble. Often called "the eagle of the Antarctic," this bold creature entertains little or no fear of man. There are a number of reports of these birds attacking men, particularly in defense of their nests. They feed on fish and other small marine

K. J. Salmon

Skua voicing protest at being disturbed.

life, and also act as scavengers. They are not only called gulls and
eagles, but also Antarctic vultures. They are none of these things
except, perhaps, in behavior. They fly like gulls, hunt like eagles,
and eat like vultures.

The habit of preying on penguin eggs and chicks seems to be
limited to certain individuals. A few skuas will set up nesting sites
near a penguin rookery and then hunt and feed. Others will choose
sites away from the rookeries and subsist on sea life. Skuas, it is
believed, always return to the same nesting site. Banding experi-
ments substantiate this belief. Besides being the only flying bird
that can be considered truly Antarctic, the skua has a couple of
other distinctions. It is believed to be the only bird that breeds
in both the Antarctic and the Arctic. Birds from both ends of our
planet (they do not migrate between the regions like the Arctic
tern) belong to the same species, and the differences between individuals from the two areas are minor. Slight variations in size and
color can be noted in careful comparison. A second distinction is the
skua's obviously accurate claim to being the world's most southern
race. Of all the animals in this whole world, the skua has been
found furthest south—within a few miles of the South Pole! Why
any bird would go that far is not known. It isn't likely that migration could account for it. *If* a skua did want to migrate to the opposite side of the continent, and this is an extremely doubtful sup-

position, it would almost certainly go around the continent and not over it. There is absolutely nothing for them to eat on the 1- to 3-mile high snow cover. There just doesn't seem to be any reasonable explanation. Getting lost is not acceptable bird behavior, and this is particularly true of birds accustomed to a rugged marine environment like Antarctic coastal regions. This is one more riddle of the far South that remains to be solved.

The skua is not a beautiful bird, neither is it very pleasant. It, somehow, seems fitting to make our last observation concerning it a negative one. The skua is a cannibal of the worst kind. They generally lay two eggs, but rarely raise more than one chick. The first nestling to wander away from the nest is pounced upon and killed by its parents. The dead chick is eaten by its parents or fed to the surviving chick. This may not happen all the time, but is often the case. Well has the skua earned his rather evil reputation.

THE INSECTS

None of the animals we have been discussing in this or the previous chapter have been land animals. The whale is totally marine, the seals spend so much time in the sea and depend on it so entirely for food that they, too, are classified as marine. Of the three Antarctic birds, one has the power of flight, and two are as marine as the seal. Is there a land animal in Antarctica?

The giant land animal of the Arctic is the polar bear, achieving a length of about eleven feet. There is a giant land animal in the Antarctic, too. He is a giant only in comparison with the other land animals, because he is about $\frac{1}{950}$ the length of a large polar bear and, roughly estimating, about 1/1,600,000 the weight of one. The largest known land animal of the Antarctic—the true giant—is a wingless mosquito!

Why anything as frail as a mosquito should survive where almost all others fail is not known. There are about 50 species of insects and insect relatives (arthropods) that have been identified, and these constitute the total land animal population so far discovered. There are non-parasitic mites and some tiny creatures known as springtails. One snowy petrel was found, carrying two biting lice safe and warm under its feathers. Snow fleas, similar to the springtails (the names are sometimes interchangeable), have been found, in very limited areas, in some variety. Some exceedingly small water bears (tardigrades) which are, of course, not bears but microscopic animals of very uncertain kinship, are found fairly regularly. Science still hasn't found the proper niche for them, but they may come close to the mites. The rest of the list resembles very closely the types we have already mentioned and wouldn't add much to our knowledge of Antarctica, if reported separately here. They are of great interest to the specialist, however; and when the research has been completed involving these tiny creatures, a great deal more may be known about the Antarctic in general. There are now some thirteen agencies involved in biological studies in Antarctica, and a great deal of effort is being spent on these arthropods.

There is, of course, a great deal of unexplored territory. It isn't likely that any chimpanzees, parrots, or boa constrictors will be found in these new areas, once they are opened up to science; but there may be a slight extension of the present population list. It is fairly certain that whatever is found will again be of great interest to the specialist and not very exciting to the general Antarctic enthusiast. Some clue to the weird and unfathomable facts that do pop up can be found in an early 1962 announcement by the National Science Foundation. They stated in a bulletin that two Kansas biologists had discovered that water from the bottom of a salty Antarctic lake (Lake Vanda) had a temperature of 71° F! We shall discuss some of these unanswered mysteries in the last chapter; but it serves our purpose to observe here that, if warm water can be found in a lake where all around it, including the earth and the air, is below freezing, we must hold off a little longer before stating positively what does and doesn't exist in the land of the South.

THE PLANTS

The list of plants in the Antarctic is about as exciting as the list of land animals. While the land fringe of the Arctic supports more than 400 species of flowering plants, all of the known Antarctic supports no more than 50 to 60 plants of any description. Two known Antarctic plants, a pink and a grass, are flowering; and these are found only far north on the Palmer Peninsula, where it reaches up toward South America. All of the other plant life consists of lichens, mosses, and some algae. Only the most primitive kind of plant seems able to survive.

It is interesting that, among both the plants and the land animals, there are no advanced races. Specialized, highly developed forms of life can't adapt. The secret of survival belongs to those organisms close to the original secret of life. Whatever life was looking for in its ascent from one-celled animals to intelligent mammals, it couldn't find it in the ice and snow of Antarctica.

127

Official U.S. Navy Photograph

Stanford University scientist probing for invertebrate specimens.

UNDER THE ICE

We talked earlier of the chain of life in the sea that supports the whale visitors from the north. Life in the seas, around the edges of the ice, and under the shelves themselves, is wonderfully abundant. These nitrate- and phosphate-rich waters support countless microscopic plants, and from these spring a long chain of ever higher life forms. Sea spiders, marine worms, corals, sponges, and many crustaceans crawl about in the bottom ooze. Even where the ice is 50 to 100 feet thick, life persists in great variety. Sea anemones, segmented worms, copepods, limpets, sea butterflies, and even octopuses have been taken where scientists have laboriously broken through the ice. Snails and clams are known to exist.

One of the unanswered mysteries of the South is the method by which the ice shelves maintain themselves. Some clues were found in 1960 when over 50 fish and other marine creatures were found, frozen in the surface ice over a mile from open water. Evidently, ice freezes all the way to the bottom during some winter seasons and then works its way up to the top in the years that follow. The sea life found at the surface of the ice may have been hundreds, and even thousands, of years old, since the ice was very thick and the water quite deep. Sponges and snails were found, along with star-fish mixed in with the frozen fish.

There are about 130 known species of actual fish around and under the Antarctic coastal ice. Some of these grow to considerable size. While this author was visiting the Antarctic, two American biologists came into possession of a fish 52 inches long, weighing 48 pounds. The method by which they took the largest fish found to that date in this part of the world wasn't exactly sporting. While walking along the ice, they were suddenly confronted by a seal, which popped up out of his hole onto the ice to enjoy his dinner. He had the big fish in his mouth. It took some time for the biologists to convince the greedy pinniped that his dinner was of greater value to science than to his appetite, but they made their point, and the laboratory gained an interesting specimen.

About 5 per cent of the entire Antarctic fish population come from families with wide geographical distribution. There are eleven species in this 5 per cent: 1 hagfish, 1 ray, 2 eel cods, 5 eel pouts and 2 snail fishes. The remaining 95 per cent belong to four families which, with the exception of one genus, are all limited to Antarctic waters. These four families belong to a group known as the noto-thenoid fishes and have the rather formidable designations of Bathydraconidae (Antarctic dragon fishes), Chaenichthyidae (Ice fishes), Harpagiferidae (Plunder fishes), and Nototheniidae (Antarctic cods). The notothenoids include one additional family, the Bovichthyidae, which is sub-Antarctic. There are some 150 to 200 sub-Antarctic fishes which are sometimes grouped with the true Antarctic species.

Of the four families of true Antarctic fishes, one family, the Chaenichthyidae, is perhaps the strangest. These fishes, commonly known as *ice fish*, were for a long time believed to be the figment of the whaling man's imagination. Returning whalers frequently referred to the strange, bloodless fish of the Antarctic with white instead of red gills. These odd creatures have no red cells and no haemoglobin in their blood! How this is possible, since they must have descended from fish with normal vertebrate blood, is not yet known.

STA. 61D

STA. 61

Official U.S. Navy Photograph

Bottom samples from Antarctic coastal waters.

Not only are the Chaenichthyidae without red cells and the all-important haemoglobin in their blood, but they are semitransparent, scaleless, and their ribs lack ossification. I think the name *Ghost-fish* would suit them even better than *Ice-fish!* The members of this weird family are generally quite small, although one species, *Chaenocephalus aceratus*, gets almost as big as his name—2 feet, 2½ pounds. All of these Ghost-fish are Antarctic, except one species which ranges to the north as far Patagonia.

Life on the Antarctic continent is sparse and, seemingly, of not great variety. Even a small park, in the heart of a great industrial city, will contain many, many times the number of types of living creatures found on the entire surface of our planet's fifth largest continent. Your own back yard is a veritable jungle by comparison. What is important, however, is that life does exist. The mysterious process common to all creatures, great and small, can be maintained. Even the harshest environment the great forces of our atmosphere can produce has been unable to wipe out life entirely. As we have pointed out, life may have to reduce itself to its simplest forms or make radical adjustments to survive, but survive it does, and the significance of this is a part of the subject matter of the next chapter.

Note: It was the author's intention to provide a comprehensive checklist of all Antarctic plants and animals. This seemed to be not only a valuable addition to this book, but also a reasonable task to undertake. The author was mistaken. No complete checklist is possible at this time. There is far too much work to be done by botanists, and zoologists, and the specialists in both general areas. A checklist was attempted, but so many footnotes, admissions of ignorance, and frank differences of opinion cluttered the pages that the task soon became hopeless. You are referred, however, to the 162-page publication of the National Academy of Sciences-National Research Council noted as Publication 839. Its title is *A Report by the Committee on Polar Research, Science in Antarctica, Part 1, The Life Sciences in Antarctica.* The simplified code is NAS-NRC 839. The Library of Congress Catalog Card Number is 61-60012. The publication carries very comprehensive articles and checklists in the several specialized fields of the life sciences. The 162 fact-packed pages of this book could not be condensed here and have any meaning, although the pages of Latin names following one upon the other would, indeed, be impressive!

8

What Does the Antarctic Mean to Man?

WE have seen that, by any set of standards, the great area at the bottom of our planet is a miserable place to work and live. We have seen that, historically, man suffered terribly and often died in his attempts just to look into her heartlands. We have seen how hazardous life still is for man in this environment. We have discussed the practically non-existent plant life and the hopelessly unproductive land-animal population. The seals are of no real value to our present way of life, and only the whales are of economic significance. Except for a brief period, little more than ten years in the early 1800's, when the fur seal was available in great numbers, the whale has always been the only valuable product the Antarctic had to offer us. But, to catch the whale you don't have to climb glaciers, build villages under the snow, and suffer the numbing cold of black Antarctic winters. What, then, does the Antarctic mean to man? What is worth the terrible price man has already paid and obviously must continue to pay?

There are many ways in which we can answer this question. Some of our answers will be cold, hard fact, obvious to the practical mind, and others will be seemingly of a more philosophical bent. The overall answer, the one answer that blankets the whole subject, is, quite simply, man *has* to conquer her. *He must.*

Let's start with the big things and focus down to the small, as we go along. The biggest thing with which we have any practical experience is our own planet—Earth. Outer space is fast entering into our concept of environment but, realistically, Mars, Venus, Jupiter, and the rest are many decades away from being of any real, practical use. Space, just now being approached, is still essentially an intellectual experience. Planet Earth, on the other hand, will be man's major concern far, far into the future. Here he will continue to live and die, and here he must support his needs and sustain his species.

What is planet Earth? It is a speck of dust in a place we must call "everywhere." It is a blink, a flash in time. It is a tiny blemish on "forever." Yet, it is our total world. We arose from its ashes and its fires, and we have set out to conquer it. We were evolved in such a way that only by the conquest of the unknown can we survive. Less than a fraction of a second ago, as the life of a planet is measured, there were just a few thousand of us on all of Earth. Now, we total close to three billion in number, and, within your own lifetime, it has been estimated, that number will *double*. We don't live on this planet alone, and many of the creatures with whom we share this pinpoint in space are inimical to our well-being. Tiny specks of life and, perhaps, of semi-life, destroy us. But man has learned how to fight back and is winning the battle against our natural enemies, the bacteria and viruses. The result is explosive—population explosive—and man is expanding at a breath-taking pace. The world is crowded now—in 40 years, when there are twice as many people, it will be jam-packed. Space, as we have pointed out, will not be able to absorb the overflow. What is the answer? Simply this: man must utilize his planet with maximum efficiency.

Nearly three-quarters of our planet is already under water and difficult of access. It was only months ago that man finally managed to penetrate its most forbidding depths. Great as that accomplishment is—the descent of a magical machine carrying two men to the bottom of a trench in the Pacific Ocean—it isn't the answer to our problem. For living space, man must utilize the remaining quarter of his globe that rises above the restless waters. From the sea, man will, one day, get a major part of his food. The Antarctic is important to both of these considerations.

That part of our planet that asserts itself above the great seas and oceans is divided into continents and islands. The distribution is often uneconomical, but over it we have no control. Some island groups contain over 3,000 separate pieces of land. Most of these

Smoothing the walls of a tunnel that will be part of a new city under the ice in Marie Byrd Land.

units are too small to be of value and are a complete waste. If this land were lumped together, man could use it. But it isn't, and much of it must be written off. The continents are a different matter, for here the earth rises out of the sea in mammoth hunks and brings with it the treasures of its chemical wonders. Here is something man can take a grip on, here he can flourish. But, remember, the fifth largest of these few continents is the subject of this book.

We haven't meant to slight the islands of the world, and many islands are great and important. The smaller ones are frequently among the most beautiful places on Earth and offer havens to man that even the mighty continents can't produce. The Antarctic has at least its share of islands. The southern islands are no more haven than the mainland is, but we must acknowledge that, no matter how you approach the problem of actual physical space, by continents or by aggregate island acreage, the Antarctic always emerges as a major consideration.

A tremendously important factor in man's rise on this planet is his adaptability. His ability to acclimate and adjust is a result of two other factors, intelligence and basic physical design. The great lesson learned in the Antarctic in the past few decades is that man, because he is adaptable, intelligent, and wondrously versatile in his structural detail, is able to survive the coldest regions the environment of this planet can produce. The temperature of 126° F below zero, measured on the polar plateau in 1959, may not be the coldest the Antarctic *ever* gets; but it is cold enough so that, once survived, it creates a major milestone in man's ability to endure. It can't get very much colder, and the margin of increase wouldn't make that much difference. Now that man has demonstrated his ability to survive, it is only left for him to create values on which he can found new life-economy concepts.

Our technology is so advanced today, that the time interval between initial accomplishment and extremely advanced utilization is a matter of only a few years. This interval is rapidly decreasing to the point where step one will lead man directly into productive results. Examine the record. Powered flight by a craft heavier than air was first accomplished in 1903. By 1914, man had turned this skill to both productive and destructive utility. The atom was controlled for the first time in 1942, and in 1954 the submarine *Nautilus* sailed from Groton, Connecticut, powered by the atom under harness. Rocketry, although an ancient art in primitive forms, came under serious study in the 1920's. By the beginning of the 1960's, man was well advanced in rocket projects that the most optimistic of fanciful writers had placed, only ten years before, in the next century. Compare all this with the lapse between the first description of electricity and the first turbine generator. What was the elapsed time between Gutenberg's Bible and books the common man could afford? More pointed examples: how much time elapsed between the time that man first straddled a log to paddle across a stream and the first time a steam vessel crossed the ocean, independent of man's muscle power and the caprices of the wind? How long between the first wheel and the automobile and diesel train? Obviously, man is only moments away from the time (if, indeed, he isn't already there!) when he need only conceive a thing to be good, to begin enjoying the anticipated fruits of the concept.

The one thing man can't do is alter the basic features of his planet. He can make minute changes, to be sure. A canal here, an irrigation project there, and perhaps a few pitiful square yards of land reclaimed from the sea (for as long as the sea decides to let him keep it!)—these aren't changes, only slight resistance movements. If man can't change the world, how shall he apply his seemingly

5000 pound roller used to compact snow run-ways.

unlimited genius? Obviously, to changing himself to fit the unalterable world. That is where the Antarctic comes in.

Man can live in the Antarctic as long as certain basic needs are met. There are affairs of physical survival that can't be ignored. The first essential is gravity to hold man to his earth; and the second, of equal importance, is air to breathe. The Antarctic provides both of these. A third essential is a tolerable temperature range, and, despite all we have said, the Antarctic provides this also. As long as man is careful in his provisions, the coldest environment known on earth is perfectly tolerable, if not exactly comfortable.

What doesn't the Antarctic offer? Food comes to mind immediately. For the time being, man can bring it with him. Later on, he will take it from the sea. It is only a matter of time before men everywhere will be feeding off the untapped food treasures, now all but totally ignored, that exist in the sea by the billion-ton units. No other sea and, as we have seen, no land is as rich in life and, therefore, nourishment as the Antarctic coastal waters. Man is learning to grow edible foodstuffs for himself and for his livestock without soil. The art of hydroponics will come to Antarctica as well.

Water is an essential that the Antarctic holds in a jealous grip. The difference between water and ice, however, is only heat, and

Official U.S. Navy Photograph

A Peter Snow Miller from Switzerland excavating for a city under the ice.

this precious commodity man now has in almost unlimited quantity. The atom is already in the far South.

On December 14, 1961, the 14,200-ton U.S.S. *Arneb* arrived at McMurdo Sound behind an escort of icebreakers. The first Antarctic nuclear reactor was unloaded onto the ice shelf, and a whole new era began. The reactor, built by the Martin Marietta Corporation of Baltimore, will give an Antarctic installation an unlimited water supply for the first time in history. The days of laboriously transporting tons of snow from uncontaminated snow mines to snow melters are on the way out. No longer will thousands of gallons of precious fuel be consumed melting this snow. Now, a heated pipe will be lowered through the thick, permanent ice shelf into the sea, and sea water will be pumped up to giant evaporators. The almost unlimited heat supply from the reactor will distill as many thousands of gallons of sweet water as the base requires. For the first time, a daily shower will be available to Antarctic explorers, scientists, and support personnel.

Another blessing atomic energy will bring to the far South is freedom from dangerous, oil-burning heating units. Up to now, each building has had to have at least one stove for heat. There was, and is, a constant danger of fire from units left unattended. These units give off fumes, and, in a shack sealed tightly against outside

137

weather, these gases can be very hazardous. Electric fans are required to circulate the air in these buildings, but headaches are still common. Now, electricity is available in great quantity. The readily convertible energy from the reactor can be put to many uses, including safe electric heaters.

The nuclear core in this first Antarctic reactor, the PM-3A, is planned to operate for a full 2 years, but might last as long as 10. It will take only three weeks to make the change, when it is finally necessary to replace it. The plant itself has been designed to operate for 20 years and will provide 1,500 kw of electrical power. A line voltage of 4,160 volts will be generated. The fuel used is highly enriched uranium, and a single core has the power output potential of 40,000 barrels of diesel oil, although it is no larger than a single oil barrel.

The first reactor went into operation early in 1962. A second reactor will be installed in the next few years at New Byrd Station in Marie Byrd Land, and a third one will operate at Amundsen-Scott Base, at the Geographic South Pole, before 1966. The snow tunnels to house the units at New Byrd are already under construction. The fourth reactor to go into operation in Antarctica during this decade will be back at McMurdo Sound. The schedule of events planned for McMurdo is so extensive, two reactors will be required!

Also in operation in the Antarctic are atomic-powered weather stations. These small units can be set in place with a minimum amount of labor and left unattended. For 10 years, the small atomic-energy units will power these stations, enabling them to broadcast regularly vital information about the ever-changing weather picture.

Soon, atomic-powered ships will ply the Antarctic Ocean. Russia already has an atomic icebreaker, the *Lenin*, in operation in the North. Atomic aircraft are just around the corner.

What will atomic energy eventually mean to Antarctica? It will make it habitable. Man will live there and, with the help of his advanced technology, thrive. We are *not* crossing over into the realm of science-fiction when we speak of cities heated by atomic power, with streets and passageways between buildings covered with plastic arches. Atomic-powered vessels will harvest the incredibly rich protein plankton from the sea, and huge, transparent barns will house racks of trays with vegetables growing in enriched water. Livestock will live in plastic-covered pastures. A crop of hay can be raised in seven days through the art of hydroponics. This tray agriculture, plus atomic energy, will give man the new continent

Official U.S. Navy Photograph

The old and the new both still work side-by-side in Antarctica.

he so desperately needs. It is a fact—man is on the verge of reclaiming 6,000,000 square miles of desperately needed land from the ice-age.

Although atomic energy is, in fact, in use in Antarctica, we have been reaching a bit into the future when we visualize the benefits it will bring. What of the present, what does man get from the Antarctic *now*, except whale oil and frostbite?

The first thing he gets, and the most important, is the future. He is pioneering, just as he is in space. He is investing in his own future, he is expressing faith in his own supreme endurance. It is true that man must conquer this land of vast dimensions in order to survive, but there is an element of psychology that, in honesty, we can't ignore. Before going on to review the present and future benefits of Antarctic exploration, we should pause and acknowledge certain facts we have rather calculatingly bypassed. We must differentiate between the generic "man," the less generalized "men," and the very specific "man," referring, in this latter case, to one individual.

Only in the sense that the race "man" created specific "men" can we say that *man* is doing this and *man* is doing that to recap-

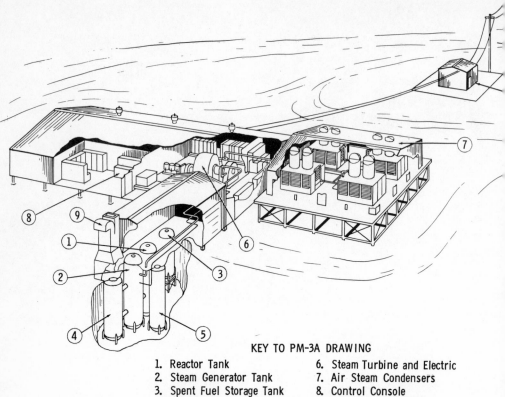

KEY TO PM-3A DRAWING

1. Reactor Tank
2. Steam Generator Tank
3. Spent Fuel Storage Tank
4. Void Tank
5. Waste System Container
6. Steam Turbine and Electric
7. Air Steam Condensers
8. Control Console
9. Shield Water Cooler
10. Electrical Substation

The Martin Marietta Corporation

The first Antarctic Nuclear Reactor.

NUCLEAR POWER PLANT RUNNING IN ANTARCTIC

Washington, March 5, 1962—(AP)—The Atomic Energy Commission's nuclear power plant at the South Pole is now in operation.

The medium-sized portable plant at McMurdo Sound, the first in the Antarctic, achieved a controlled, self-sustained chain reaction Saturday afternoon, the commission reported yesterday.

After further tests, the plant will be used to produce 1,500 net kilowatts of electricity at McMurdo, the principal support base for all U.S. scientific activities in the Antarctic.

The plant will reduce the need for fuel oil, a costly item because it has to be hauled great distances.

ture the Antarctic from the ice-age. *Men* have done it, a few men brave and true. We discussed heroics a few chapters back and came to the conclusion, you will recall, that the "hey-look-at-me" kind of guy was far more trouble than he was worth, in an environment as hazardous as the Antarctic. We must not deny, however, that it takes a man with a certain sense of destiny to dedicate his life to high mountains, creeping glaciers, and deadly blizzards.

Fortunately, man manages, even when the living is easy, to produce a few of these men in each generation. We are speaking of the kind of man who can't let a challenge go by. Since the title of this chapter asks the question, "What does the Antarctic mean to man?", we must sandwich in here, between observations on future and present Antarctic economy, the idea that the great South means a *challenge* to man. Psychologically, it has been a bit of a thorn in his side. It has dared him and taunted him and goaded him on. If the Antarctic has given man nothing else, it has given him a goal and not just a few heroes. We must not underestimate the value of either of these!

We have referred, on a number of occasions in these pages, to Antarctica's 6,000,000 square miles. Square miles of what? Generally speaking, 6,000,000 square miles of ice-covered continent. Specifically, we are not very well informed about most of that vast area. Too little rock is bare for us to make any generalizations about what the whole may, or may not, contain. This much, by way of specific information, we do know—16 minerals of potential commercial value have already been uncovered. Extensive coal deposits have been found, and uranium-bearing ore was identified on the Prince Olav Coast by a Japanese expedition.

Oceanography will probably give us more information about the geological composition of the main land mass than pure geology itself. Core samples of sediment, dredged up from the sea in the canyons of prehistoric Antarctic rivers, are likely to show the true make-up of the continent, since these rivers once carried Antarctic silt into the sea. These investigations are now in progress.

Antarctica is rich in fossils: Stems, fragmentary impressions of wood, and tropical ferns have been found in quantity. We will discuss some of the great mysteries that spring from these finds in the next chapter, but we should note here that the Antarctic was once tropical or, at least, semi-tropical. Does this mean oil? It could, but we don't know. Sandstone and coal have been found within 300 miles of the Pole itself. Some high-quality anthracite has been located in good-sized seams. Oil may be there, too. It certainly is a possibility worth examining.

Gold, copper, lead, chromium, molybdenum, antimony, zinc, and tin have been found, although, admittedly, not yet in exploitable quantities. At least, we know they are there, perhaps in vast quantities, in areas not yet tested, which is most of the continent. There are "oases," areas where the ground is bare; and these areas may reveal much, once the surface has been scratched. One "oasis," in South Victoria land, covers 5,000 square miles.

Marble and granite exist over wide areas and, it is believed, in great quantity. Russian scientists found great masses of white quartz; mica, graphite, iron, and apatite, rich in phosphorous compounds, were also identified in 1959. In a nutshell, less than one-half of 1 per cent of Antarctica has been examined geologically. Very, very little is known about what is and is not there. With minor exceptions, only traces have been found, and these have been too scattered to permit any conclusions to be drawn. One interesting exception was a statement by Lawrence M. Gould, president of Carleton College in Minnesota. In a 1957 issue of *The Geographical Review* (Vol. XLVII, No. 1) he indicated that there *may be* more coal in the Beacon Sandstone formation in Antarctica than in all the rest of the world together. Much of the coal, he points out, is low-grade and not generally accessible.

What if rich mineral deposits are located on the southernmost land mass? Could man profit from them? The same factors that make geological exploration difficult would make exploitation a thousand times more so. For the moment, the Antarctic's mineral wealth, if it exists, is as much a part of the future as are its cities under plastic domes. There can be little doubt that man *could* mine the Antarctic if he wanted to—and if he finds something to mine—however, for the present, the cost would so far exceed the profit that it won't be done. Only when man's need is so great that he cannot do without, will he invest the money and effort required to exploit so difficult a region in this way. It would be comforting to know, however, that Antarctica did have deposits of metals and fuels we could fall back on, if and when we use up the more accessible sources. Perhaps the next few years will give us that comfort.

In our generalized description of Antarctica in Chapter 1, we described it as "a restless and monstrous refrigeration plant." This is a prime motivating factor in man's continuing interest in the area. Weather is one product of the Antarctic continent for which man does *not* have to wait. Although he has just realized it in recent

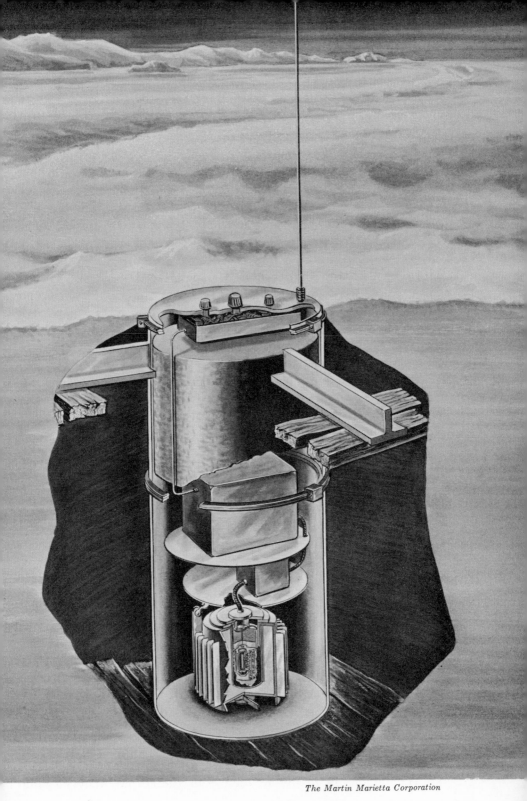

A nuclear-powered automatic weather station.

years, Antarctic weather forces have always been with us. Our lives have been greatly affected by them, and our understanding of them has now become an essential to our way of life.

There was a time, in the quite recent past, when a storm or a day of calm were considered purely local phenomena. Men did not appreciate the complex interconnecting factors involved and could only predict weather on the basis of past local behavior and rough statistical analysis. Sailing men were, perhaps, more advanced than any other single group, but even they were limited to a generalized knowledge of seasons in certain areas and the interpretation of local signs. The concept of real prediction, based on world-wide factors, had to wait until it became possible to get information around the world as soon as it was available. Modern travel and communication not only make world-wide forecasting possible, but they supply a principal motivation for accomplishing it. Man's technology will probably never advance to the point where he will be able to ignore the weather. He will always be subject to it, even after he understands it completely. His power to control it will, no doubt, expand, but his ability will, almost certainly, be limited to relatively small areas. Weather, Antarctica's principal export, is here to stay!

Antarctica, we know, is the coldest and the windiest place on our planet. As such, it is a nursery for world weather. The things that happen there over the surface of the ice not only govern the degree of comfort the local explorer will have, but also dictate the kind of plants and the kind of animal life that will flourish thousands of miles to the north.

There is a constant interchange at the surface of great bodies of water. Gases are absorbed into the bosom of the sea, while the sea releases moisture into the air. Moisture leaving the sea for the air is making only a very temporary change. Sooner or later, this moisture will come down as rain, sleet, or snow and greatly affect the life and economy of the area on which it descends. The rate at which moisture is drawn into the air is greatly affected by the temperature of the air and the temperature of the water. The frequency with which it is released from the air over a given area is largely affected not only by the amount of water in the air, but by the so-called "fronts," the hot and cold masses of moving air with which every television viewer is familiar. You will recall that hot and cold fronts generally occur midway between sports scores and a message from the local bank or utility company.

The billions upon untold billions of tons of ice that surround

144

the Antarctic continent, and are constantly being renewed by its glaciers, cannot help but markedly affect the seas and oceans. Masses of cold water stream northward, altering the precipitation rate and the annual temperature means of every continent and island they pass. They extend the range of some sea creatures and restrict the distribution of others. Plant life, everywhere affected by moisture and temperature, also is controlled in its distribution by the presence or absence of cold oceanic currents. None of man's economy, on land, in the sea, or in the air, is free from the effects of these rivers within the sea.

Masses of air are constantly on the move over the Antarctic ice. The great glaciers that lead from the high polar plateau to the sea, often descending two or more miles to get there, are natural toboggan slides for these frigid air masses. These bitter winds increase in intensity as they slip downward toward the sea and scream outward across the coastal ice and water at twice minimum hurricane force. These aren't gusts and blasts, such as are encountered elsewhere. For hours, days, and even weeks on end, this mass of heavy, icy air roars down and out to the north. The wind systems of the world are violently affected by this avalanche of wind, and our whole planet feels the effects.

Man has progressed beyond the point where good weather is a convenience and bad weather a nuisance. He has always been concerned with weather because of his dependence on agriculture and his fishing fleets. But now, the very way of life we depend on depends, in turn, on communication and transportation. Long-distance transportation and communication are directly affected by the weather—weather that is created in the polar regions. No other single science in the Antarctic has been afforded the time and effort that meteorology has. On the surface of the ice, over the plateau, carried aloft by balloons, and high above in rockets, instruments broadcast tons of data back to man and his recorders. One day, the electronic brains will consume and digest these mountains of facts and figures, and out of them will come an understandable pattern. The constants will be established, the variables predicted, and the statistics extended far enough to give man a workable tool. Here are a few projects now in progress:

The temperature and wind profiles in the upper atmosphere, to an altitude of 200,000 feet, are being drawn, using the 92-inch-long Arcas rocket as an instrument vehicle. Since ozone from the north has been detected in Antarctica during the winter, it is probable that there are high-altitude, southbound winds during the dark

A 9-ton Caterpillar tractor being dropped over Antarctic ice. Plane is C-124 Globemaster.

and frozen months. The importance of these heretofore unknown winds can be determined only by investigating them at their own level. The rocket probes will do this, 12 months of the year.

The albedo is the quantity of light reflected from a surface, the amount of solar energy striking Earth that is not immediately absorbed. An intensive study of this Antarctic "heat budget" is under way, and, from it, a better understanding of the numerous intense cyclones along the periphery of the Antarctic should emerge. A more complete knowledge of the growth of the ice sheet in winter, and the effect this has on world storm patterns, is also expected to come from this study.

The content and variability of carbon dioxide in the earth's atmosphere has long been a concern of man. Our understanding of this gas and its exchange rate is considered essential to an overall understanding of our atmosphere and the forces that shape it. No study of this problem could be complete without a constant supply of data from the Antarctic. The station at the South Pole itself is involved in this project.

On and on it goes. Using advanced electronic and mechanical equipment, highly skilled and dedicated specialists, living often under terrible conditions, work to expand man's knowledge just a little farther. Each new factor is recorded and fitted to the giant jigsaw puzzle that is the world's weather. Surface and upper air, energy balance, radiometersonde observations, ozone, water vapor, snow density, and snow drift—all of these, and many more, are the everyday concern of a very new kind of Antarctic explorer.

Man is now involved in the continuous recording of the strange happenings deep inside our planet. We can no longer be satisfied with knowledge of the surface alone. The plans we are making for our future survival call for our gaining all the knowledge there is to be had. We now have relatively little knowledge about the interior of our planet. Only when the great natural spectacles occur—the volcanos and earthquakes—or when we witness scattered natural phenomena like hot springs, great scenic caves, and boiling mud, do we, the average citizens, think of what is going on beneath our feet. To the specialists, this matter of Earth's inner layers is of constant interest and concern. Perhaps, if man hadn't rather arbitrarily put heaven above and hell below, he would have spent more time looking down and less up. Be that as it may, man is now looking down and doing more than scratching his head.

Webster defines *seismology* as "the science of earthquakes and attendant phenomena." "Attendant phenomena" covers a multitude of sins, and some of these sins are best attended to in the Antarctic. Man could not maintain a running record of the forces at work deep within his planet without making studies of its fifth largest continent. The fact that this world-wide study is in progress, is reason enough to have scientific stations in the far South. There is, however, a second good reason. There is something unusual going on in Antarctica—an entire continent is being depressed! Antarctica is being weighed down, forced down by the almost incalculable quantity of ice resting on its back. In some places, the continent may actually be 2 or 3 thousand feet lower than its original level, as a result of this crushing weight. The plasticity of the Earth can, to a degree, be demonstrated by this fact. The significance of this is not limited to the Antarctic alone. If continents react this way to ice ages as a matter of course (and they almost certainly do!), then North America and Northern Europe must still be in the process of springing back into shape from the last period of glaciation in those areas. It is believed, for example, that portions of Finland rise about three feet every century. The end result of all this is that the coastlines of areas, only relatively recently freed from ice, are not fixed but will continue to adjust. Rivers will be deflected from their seemingly established courses, and land will rise out of the sea and be available to man.

It seems fairly certain that something like this is going on. The surface of our planet is undulating, sinking and rising with the great ice tides.

The controller of this pulse is the ice whose weight causes it, although the factors that, in turn, control the ice can be said to be the master controls of it all. In the Northern hemisphere, we have vast areas just now emerging from an ice age. In the Antarctic, we have an equally vast expanse of land still locked tight in the grip of an ice age, although we aren't certain in which direction the trend is, at this moment, headed. Even without a positive answer to this last question, it is apparent that a complete analysis of the ice age in Antarctica is absolutely essential to any kind of understanding of our planet.

Early in 1962, a meteorite, the size of a basketball, was found on the surface of the snow about 330 miles from the South Pole. Quite a fuss was made about this find, it being, probably, the largest meteorite ever found in Antarctica. As interesting as meteorites are, they are probably the least exciting of all the particles that bombard the surface of Earth from outer space. The other particles never achieve the size of a basketball but have a far greater effect

A balloon carries a radiosonde aloft at the South Pole.

on our lives. The particles we are speaking of are energy particles, and no place on the surface of our planet offers a better laboratory for their study than the polar regions. *Upper-atmosphere physics* constitutes a major Antarctic study project.

The Earth, as we all know, is enclosed in a magnetic field. It is, in itself, a huge spherical magnet, and its field runs roughly parallel with its surface over most of the globe. The exceptions are at the Geomagnetic Poles, for here the magnetic field dips down and ends up running virtually straight up and down from the surface of the planet.

High-energy particles, approaching our planet from outer space, crash into this magnetic field and are deflected by it. This is particularly true of the little-understood cosmic rays. Very few particles manage to penetrate this field, compared with the number approaching us from distant high-energy sources. Particles deflected by the Earth's magnetic field slip around the Earth until they approach the area above the Geomagnetic Pole. At this juncture the particles climb aboard a magnetic toboggan run and crash downward to the surface of Earth. This aspect of space, at least, is best studied in outer space itself, or at the Geomagnetic Poles.

Long, long before upper-atmosphere physics was ever dreamed of, and ages before the Polar regions were known to exist, man was worshipping strange polar phenomena known as *aurora*. These beautiful polar lights are a product of the sun. Extremely-high-energy particles, exploded toward us out of the sun, bombard our upper atmosphere, causing the disintegration of minute particles of matter already there. The energy released in this breaking-down process is seen as light. Great rays, arcs, and multi-colored draperies loop across the polar skies, visible for thousands of miles. What pagan priests once worshipped, scientists now study with keen interest. Man comes closer to outer space in the polar regions than at any other place on the surface of our planet.

There are a great many studies tied up with our atmosphere that benefit greatly from Antarctic scientific installations. Strange radio sounds, known as whistlers, are under intensive study. Aurora, air glow, cosmic radiation, geomagnetism, ionosphere studies, and a long list of even more formidable-sounding projects are only part of it. All science is today interrelated. No part can be completely removed from the whole, and there is no place *more* important to the study of the whole than the Antarctic.

The modern systems of communication and travel that man has developed to make his stay on earth more pleasant and meaningful

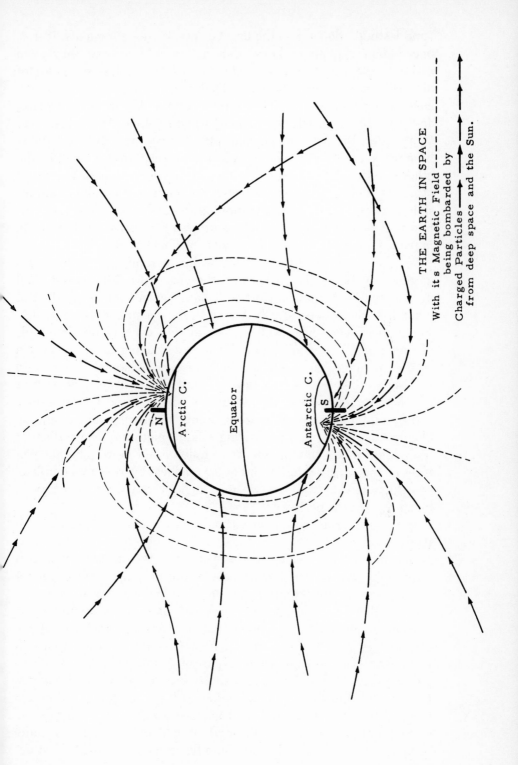

THE EARTH IN SPACE

With it's Magnetic Field - - - - - - -
being bombarded by
Charged Particles ━━━▶ ━━━▶
from deep space and the Sun.

(and lasting!) depend on the finest of precise measurements. It was, once, good enough to know that a certain river ran through a certain valley, and that the valley was more or less southeast of an easily recognized landmark. That was during the days of the covered wagon, when it took forever and a day to go any place, any way. But man left the covered wagon behind. With it, he had to abandon his inadequate concepts of place and distance. Now, he must know exactly where a place is in relationship to all of the other exactly placed features on the surface of the Earth. The speed of his vehicles, however, increased much more rapidly than his skill at mapping. He is just beginning to catch up. It is almost certain that man will start to chart and map the surface of the moon, *in person,* long before he is done with his home planet.

Nowhere is man farther behind in his map-making than in Antarctica—except at the bottom of the sea. This fifth largest land mass is the least known. Most of it hasn't even been seen. Most of what has been "seen" really hasn't been, because it is under ice. Remember, when you walk across an ice cake many thousands of feet thick, you don't know if you are walking across a hidden mountain range, an ice-filled valley, or a sea channel frozen solid and separating two islands with a strait of ice instead of a strait of sea water. You don't, that is, unless you stop and take measurements, and that is what man is doing, measuring and mapping. Slowly but surely, man is drawing a finite picture of the surface of his world. When this picture is complete, and corresponding pictures of the earth's interior and outer reaches of space are complete, who knows what wonders we may behold and what new joys in living we may experience?

We could easily go on for as many pages again as we have already used in this chapter, and barely touch on the scientific experiences men are having in the Antarctic. We started out in this chapter by saying that the whale was the only apparent export of economic value the Antarctic had to offer. We went on to point out that weather was an export in a very real sense, the economic repercussions of which far exceeded that of whale oil, and whalebone corset stays, and brush handles. I hope by now, however, that you know what the most important export of Antarctica really is. There are two ways of describing this export—*knowledge* or *man's chances for survival*—but they really are one and the same thing. Once man decided to tackle his world, and not just go along for the ride, he started himself on a road the end of which he has never quite been able to visualize. The one thing he seemed to know by instinct

152

was that knowledge, ever greater and more encompassing knowledge, was the key to survival. Each step that man has taken has not only led him to the next, but forced him to take it. Finally, as we pointed out, he arrived at the place where he had beaten back death itself far enough so that that part of the world that was easily accessible was no longer enough. The next step he had to take was the total utilization of his planet. That is the step he is now taking, and Antarctica is a major part of that step.

When we said, at the beginning of this chapter, that man *had to* conquer Antarctica, we were being quite literal. Man can no more ignore this region than he can the oceans, the deserts, or the clouds overhead. Man's survival, now that he has come this far, is dependent on his ability to finish what he has started—the complete examination of all natural phenomena. He can't stop where he is, because he has increased his life expectancy and, therefore, his population growth-rate, to the point where he will soon eat up his world, unless he expands it and keeps his rate of intellectual and economic expansion several steps ahead of his entirely predictable population expansion. This is not idle speculation but cold, hard fact. Fact that is as cold and hard as Antarctica itself—Antarctica, a major component and a major goal in man's species-preserving scientific growth. No matter where you live, no matter what you do, Antarctica is as much a part of your future and the future of your descendants as the farm crops not yet sown and the rain that is yet to fall. Antarctica is no more remote from your world than the days on the pages of the calendar you are yet to turn; for as surely as those pages must be turned, so will the once remote Southern Continent be a part of man's future course on planet Earth.

9

The Unsolved Mysteries of the South

W HEN we approached the Antarctic at the beginning of this book, the chances were we each did so with some questions in mind. Man has always approached the Antarctic with questions, for the answers to which he sometimes had to give his life. The explorers who found their answers and survived always came away with not only new information but new questions, many more than they had when they started out. All worthwhile human experiences are that way. The more we learn, the more we realize how little we know. That is one way to judge the intelligence of a man, not by the answers he has, but by the questions he asks. A true scientist or a true explorer will only discuss the answers he knows when cornered and forced to do so by your questions. He would much rather discuss the questions that are bothering him. By asking, he learns and so do we.

This chapter, and this book, have been designed to leave you scratching your head for two reasons. First, there is going to be more and more said about the Antarctic, as time goes on. Books, magazine articles, newspaper accounts, radio, television, and motion pictures will steadily bombard you with reports of man's progress in the far South. This wealth of new information will have more meaning for you if you can judge it in relation to the still unsolved mysteries. You have to be able to match an answer to a question before you can weigh its value. The second reason for leaving you with questions hanging in mid-air is touched on lightly in my note to you before Chapter 1. I firmly believe there is no greater impetus for looking to the life ahead than a blank map. Perhaps you will find yourself wanting to find some answers on your own. Some of the answers you might seek can be found only in the Antarctic. Others, however, relating directly to the Antarctic, can be found in laboratories and libraries far away from the snow and ice.

In earlier chapters, we posed some questions that haven't been answered. Why do seals go inland only to die of starvation? Why do they struggle over miles of jagged terrain, when each mile further assures their doom? Why are skuas found flying within twenty miles of the South Pole, when the nearest food, mate, and nesting site is 800 miles away? Why and how do penguins travel around an entire frozen continent to return to their native rookeries? Why do they pass thousands and tens of thousands of their kind in dozens of rookeries, indistinguishable from their own, to seek out the place where they were born? How is it that a fragile mosquito can survive Antarctic extremes while strong and versatile animals, of far greater endurance, have failed?

What mineral wealth does the Antarctic possess? How cold does it really get when it hits bottom? What were Captain Larsen's little clay artifacts doing off the Palmer Peninsula? How can it be that early maps, maps compiled long before the first known expeditions, show Antarctica both snowbound and free from ice? Does Antarctica have a history about which we know nothing? Why did the Antarctic, long before its real importance was known, draw men to it with such a hypnotic power that the threat of death itself was not enough to keep them away? Those are some of the questions we left hanging; now let's dig up a few more.

For sheer size and scope, as well as world-wide significance, no question is more gripping than the direction of the ice age trend in Antarctica. Is the ice sheet advancing or retreating? If it is retreating, we know that our oceans will rise from the newly released water and start to drown our present coastlines. At the same time, the Antarctic continent will rise higher out of the sea, as the great weight of the ice is reduced. If the ice sheet is advancing, much more water will be sucked out of the sea to be deposited in the Antarctic as snow and ice. Antarctica will sink yet farther into the Earth's plastic interior. Will this, in turn, cause physical stresses, the repercussions of which will be felt elsewhere? Will new lands rise out

155

of the sea and become available to man? Is the ice age in Antarctica offset by an opposite trend in the North? There are dozens more questions that stem from the first one, but let's go back to it and see what some of the contemporary thinking is like. Is the ice sheet in Antarctica advancing or retreating?

Dr. Pyotr Shoumsky, a noted Russian polar expert, announced in 1960 that the ice is *growing* at the rate of 293 cubic miles a year. It is suggested that this might be a result of the general warming of the world's weather. Such a change in climate could increase the amount of moisture-laden air being delivered to the South. The Russian glaciologist went on to say that snowfall was adding 612 cubic miles to the continent yearly! Some snow is evaporated, some is blown out to sea by the hurricane winds pouring off the ice sheet, but the biggest loss is in the form of icebergs. The total loss, he estimates, stands at 319 cubic miles every twelve months, leaving the surplus at 293 cubic miles. Dr. Malcolm Mellors, an Australian scientist, agreed with the Russian's findings, and Dr. F. Loewe, a French expert, came to the same conclusions. In some areas, it is estimated, 1,400,000 tons of snow are blown to sea each year *across each kilometer* (0.621 mile) of coastline. Some ice shelves are delivering ice to the sea at the rate of several feet a day across a front hundreds of miles long and at a depth or thickness of 800 feet. The Ross Ice Shelf, the largest in the world, covers nearly 197,000 square miles. It varies in thickness from about 325 to more than 13,000 feet. It is moving to sea at a rate of 5½ feet *per day* across a 400-mile front!

Despite all of this, a booklet called *Australians in the Antarctic,* produced for the Antarctic Division of Australia's Department of External Affairs says, "at present it is not clear whether the great bulk of the continental ice sheet is diminishing or increasing." Although Antarctica is believed to be carrying 7,000,000 cubic miles of ice, there are ice-free areas. In the last chapter, we referred to the South Victoria Land "oasis" where 5,000 square miles of the continent are virtually free from ice. There are many more ice-free valleys with clear signs that glaciers are retreating. In an information sheet describing gravity studies, the National Science Foundation poses the question, "Is the Antarctic icecap growing or shrinking?" as its lead-in sentence. The one thing that is clear is that the icecap is not fixed and stable. Something is happening to it, and whatever that is will greatly affect all of mankind. No one can say for certain, at this point, whether the Antarctic ice age is growing or diminishing. It is a very important question, but the answer has not yet been found.

All through this book, we have been referring to Antarctica as *a* continent. But, is it? Is what we know as the Antarctic mainland all one piece of land or is it two big islands? Or three? Here is another subject on which opinions are divided. Scientists making seismic soundings, using high explosives to produce the shock waves, have found places where the ice is two miles deep but the surface is only a mile above sea level. The ice goes a mile below sea level! Does this mean that the weight of the ice has pushed the continent down a full mile, dropping a valley floor that far below normal, or does it mean that a strait exists that separates two pieces of land? These surprising ice thicknesses occur too often to be ignored. There obviously exists some great factor of Antarctica's past we haven't yet discovered. There may be two Antarctic continents, separated by a narrow frozen strait, or one Antarctica plus a series of islands, the total area of which we have been calling one continent. The answers aren't in yet, and there really isn't any good reason for accepting one theory over another. Until the profile of the underlying rock has been completely drawn, and until the depth to which the continent has been weighed down is known, no answer is possible. It must remain, for the present, on the long list of unknowns.

We have already mentioned, in another chapter, the strange warm-water lakes of Antarctica. Ground heat, sun-ray concentration, and volcanic activity have all been proposed as possible explanations. Here, again, there is no positive answer available. Antarctica is the home of volcanic activity. As I write this chapter, pieces of volcanic ash and lava sit on piles of notes on my desk. These proofs of volcanic activity come from the Antarctic. A geologist, stationed near the spot where I collected the samples on Ross Island, told me they came from an eruption that occurred around 450 years ago. What other volcanos exist? Will the ever-smoking Mt. Erebus erupt again, and what will the effect of millions of tons of molten rock on billions of tons of frozen water be? If volcanic activity is going on near the surface, could this incredible quantity of heat energy be directed and channeled to make Antarctica a better place to live? Again, who knows?

Early in 1960, ice cores were being taken near the South Pole to assist in writing the history of the ice cover. This icecap has always been regarded as sterile, completely free from life. Life was believed to exist only near the continent's edge. Imagine the surprise of Lieutenant Sidney Tolchin of Easton, Pennsylvania, when he put samples of ice taken a hundred feet down under a microscope and found life! The Navy doctor found staphylococcus, a type of bacteria often dangerous to man, in a state of suspended animation. When the germs were warmed, they came to life and began to multiply. The questions that spring from this discovery are almost overwhelming. How did the germs get there? How long had they been there? How did they survive an average temperature of 65° below zero for a century or, perhaps, many centuries? Most intriguing of all—if these specks of life can survive, can others? Will deep cores bring up prehistoric life forms that have lain dormant in a kind of icy time-capsule? Will future exploration into the heart of the ice produce eggs that can be hatched to release, in this day and age, prehistoric forms of animal life?

There have been many theories, brought forth in recent years, based on the assumption that the continents have not always been where they are now. The idea of continental drift is not really so far-fetched, when you stop and recall that we already know that continents rise and sink with ice-tides. If they go up and down, perhaps they go sideways as well. Antarctica was rich in plant life in the past. Either the continent was not in its present relationship to the sun because the axis on which the Earth spins was elsewhere, or because the continent itself was. One of the two seems almost certain to have been the case. There is evidence that the Earth's spin-pole moves. Perhaps it has moved a great deal, but I rather favor the theory that continents shift. Earth, we know, hasn't stabilized yet. It probably hasn't been here for much over 4 billion years, and we know it is both slowing down its speed of spinning and cooling off in internal temperatures. There is no reason to assume that its exterior features are in their final resting places. If the interior is plastic enough to allow a 6,000,000-square-mile hunk of land to sink down from the weight of 7,000,000 cubic miles of ice, perhaps it is plastic enough to let the continent slip slowly sideways as well. A certain magnetic rock, peculiar to Australia, has been found in Antarctica. This would seem to suggest that the two land masses were once joined. On the other hand, fossil plants, found in the Antarctic, match up with plants found in South America. Scientists have long been puzzled over plant similarities in Australia and South America. Could the Antarctic have been a land bridge between the two? Of the 46 families of plants found in the forests of Chile, 39 are found 5,000 miles away in New Zealand. As you proceed northward from the tip of South America, you pass through plant zones nearly always duplicated across the Pacific in New Zealand, Tasmania, and Australia. In the moss of the Chilean beech forests are tiny insects, found in corresponding locales across the Pacific, but nowhere else in the world. Certain dragonflies are known only in these two places, separated by the greatest body of water in the world. Stoneflies, May flies, scorpion flies, some beetles, and certain fresh-water fish are also parallel and increase the mystery. Science has long wondered about a biological route.

You can't arbitrarily push whole continents back and forth like barges, just to make it easy for ferns and beetles to get around. Before you seriously suggest that the Antarctic was a biological route across the bottom of the world, the fossil records north of the areas in question must be thoroughly examined. If no fossils of these particular plants and animals are found to the north, then we can rule out the idea that they were world-wide in distribution and ended up in the southern extremes in recent times. We have to look for a means of distribution. When Antarctica was ice-free, did she ride far enough up to bring island chains out of the ocean with her? Or, did she actually move from one side of the world to the other? In which direction?

At the beginning of this book, we described Antarctica as being the *highest, coldest, and windiest continent on Earth.* Let's revise that and call her *the most perplexing, confusing, and confounding maybe continent.* We don't know how long she has been where she is or what she is. We don't know what her role has been in the distribution of the world's plants and animals, and we don't know what her resources are. There will be several more decades of hard, grueling labor, under extreme hardship, with attendant loss of life, before we can even make up an intelligent list of what we don't know. In many cases, we don't even know enough to ask questions.

The battle between man and Antarctica was decided many years ago. Man will win. But before he does, he will have to produce a lot of very special men with that very special kind of mind that absolutely demands answers. We *can* predict that the answers Antarctica will finally give up will be fascinating, even if we *can't* predict what they will be. Man and Antarctica are tied together by destiny for as long as they both shall survive. The only power that can separate them is the power that can destroy them, and then it wouldn't matter very much, would it!

Appendices

1

The Twelve-Nation Antarctic Treaty

THE twelve-nation Antarctic Treaty (see Chapter 3) is a diplomatic document of far-reaching significance. The provisions of this instrument free the world's fifth largest continent from artificial boundaries and create, instead, an international laboratory from which all mankind may benefit. The genius of the world has been set free from meaningless restrictions imposed by individual national interests. Following is a reprint from the December 21, 1959 issue of the *Department of State Bulletin,* containing the text of this treaty.

TWELVE NATIONS SIGN TREATY GUARANTEEING NONMILITARIZATION OF ANTARCTICA AND FREEDOM OF SCIENTIFIC INVESTIGATION *

Department Announcement

Press release 827 dated December 1

The United States and 11 other nations signed the Antarctic treaty at Washington on December 1. The treaty, which was negotiated during the past 6 weeks, is based upon the principles that Antarctica

* Reprinted from the *Department of State Bulletin,* December 21, 1959, Office of Public Services, Bureau of Public Affairs, by permission.

will be used for peaceful purposes only and that the international scientific cooperation which characterized the 1957–58 International Geophysical Year should continue.

The conference called to negotiate the treaty was convened at the initiative of the U.S. Government. On May 3, 1958, President Eisenhower announced that invitations had been extended to the Governments of the 11 nations which had carried on scientific research programs in Antarctica during the International Geophysical Year to participate in a conference with a view to writing a treaty "dedicated to the principle that the vast uninhabited wastes of Antarctica shall be used only for peaceful purposes."[1]

The following nations were invited: Argentina, Australia, Belgium, Chile, France, Japan, New Zealand, Norway, the Union of South Africa, the Union of Soviet Socialist Republics, and the United Kingdom.

At the treaty-signing ceremony, Herman Phleger, the U.S. representative, and Paul C. Daniels, alternate U.S. representative, signed for the United States.

The treaty will not go into effect until it has been ratified by the 12 Governments. As regards the United States, this ratification would require the advice and consent of the Senate in accordance with constitutional processes. The instrument of ratification is issued by the President after a resolution of approval is agreed to by a two-thirds vote of the Senate.

The treaty consists of a preamble and 14 articles. The treaty provides that an area of the world as large as the United States and Europe together will be used for peaceful purposes only. An effective and unprecedented system of inspection on the Antarctic Continent is envisaged. Cooperative scientific research will be continued in the Antarctic region subject to the provisions of the treaty. Until a general international agreement on nuclear explosions is reached, such explosions will be prohibited in Antarctica.

The treaty is of indefinite duration, but after 30 years any party may call a conference for review and amendment. The treaty provides that all territorial and sovereignty claims and the position of all the Governments regarding their recognition or nonrecognition of such claims shall remain in *status quo* for the period of the treaty. The treaty is open to accession by other U.N. members and by such other states as may be agreed upon unanimously.

---

[1] For a statement by the President and text of the U.S. note addressed to the Foreign Ministers of the 11 countries, see BULLETIN of June 2, 1958, p. 910.

In order to further the purposes and the objectives of the treaty a consultative committee will be established and will meet within 2 months of the entry into force of the treaty and at suitable intervals thereafter to recommend measures to the participating parties. The first meeting will be at Canberra, Australia. In the meantime the conference recommended that representatives of the Governments meet at Washington at convenient times to discuss such arrangments as they might deem desirable.

The Conference on Antarctica convened at Washington October 15, 1959.[2] At the first plenary session held that day, Herman Phleger, the U.S. representative, was named the chairman of the conference, and Henry E. Allen, the Secretary General. Paul C. Daniels and George H. Owen were alternate U.S. representatives.

U.S. interest in Antarctica dates from the early part of the 19th century. One of the earliest achievements was the 1838–42 expedition of Lt. Charles Wilkes, which made sightings extending for 1,500 miles, thus proving the existence of the Antarctic Continent.

The period from 1928 to the present has been one of great activity. The names of Rear Adm. Richard E. Byrd, Lincoln Ellsworth, Capt. Finn Ronne, and Rear Adm. R. H. Cruzen became intimately linked to Antarctica during this period. The U.S. Navy in 1946–47 organized the largest U.S. expedition to Antarctica. During the International Geophysical Year the United States established seven stations in Antarctica under the leadership of Rear Adm. George Dufek. At the present time four stations are being maintained, including one at the South Pole.

Scientific research in the Antarctic, coordinated and planned by the National Science Foundation, is made possible through the logistic support of the Navy Department, with its long experience in polar operations. The U.S. Naval Support Force is commanded by Rear Adm. David N. Tyree.

Statement by President Eisenhower[3]

I am gratified that the Antarctic treaty is being signed today in Washington by the representatives of 12 nations. This treaty is the result of the arduous and painstaking efforts of many people who for 2 years have worked to achieve this agreement of great importance to the world.

[2] For a welcoming address by Secretary Herter and a list of the heads of delegations, see *ibid.*, Nov. 2, 1959, p. 650.

[3] Read to the representatives who signed the Antarctic treaty by Secretary Herter on Dec. 1 (press release 829).

The Conference on Antarctica was convened October 15, 1959, as a result of a United States note of invitation, dated May 2, 1958, to those nations which had participated in scientific research in Antarctica during the 1957–58 International Geophysical Year.

The spirit of cooperation and mutual understanding which the 12 nations and their delegations exhibited in drafting a treaty of this importance should be an inspiring example of what can be accomplished by international cooperation in the field of science and in the pursuit of peace.

This treaty guarantees that a large area of the world will be used only for peaceful purposes, assured by a system of inspection. Antarctica will constitute a laboratory for cooperative scientific research in accordance with treaty provisions. The legal *status quo* there will be maintained for the duration of the treaty. Nuclear explosions are prohibited pending general international agreement on the subject.

The Antarctic treaty and the guarantees it embodies constitute a significant advance toward the goal of a peaceful world with justice.

Statement by Secretary Herter[4]

The Governments of the United States of America, Argentina, and Chile, on the occasion of the signing of the Antarctic treaty, declare that the Antarctic treaty does not affect their obligations under the Inter-American Treaty of Reciprocal Assistance, signed at Rio de Janeiro, Brazil, in 1947.[5]

Text of Final Act

The Governments of Argentina, Australia, Belgium, Chile, the French Republic, Japan, New Zealand, Norway, the Union of South Africa, the Union of Soviet Socialist Republics, the United Kingdom of Great Britain and Northern Ireland, and the United States of America.

Having accepted the invitation extended to them on May 2, 1958, by the Government of the United States of America to participate in a Conference on Antarctica to be attended by representatives of the twelve nations which cooperated in the Antarctic Program of the International Geophysical Year;

Appointed their respective Representatives, who are listed below by countries:

[4] Released on Dec. 1 (press release 831).
[5] 62 Stat. 1681.

ARGENTINA

Representative
His Excellency
Adolfo Scilingo
(Head of Delegation)
Alternate Representative
Dr. Francisco R. Bello

AUSTRALIA

Representatives
The Right Honorable
Richard Gardiner Casey, C.H.,
D.S.O., M.C., M.P.
(Head of Delegation)
His Excellency the Honorable
Howard Beale, Q.C.
(Deputy Head of Delegation)
Alternate Representatives
J. C. G. Kevin
M. R. Booker

BELGIUM

Representative
His Excellency
Viscount Obert de Thieusies
(Head of Delegation)
Alternate Representatives
Jean de Bassompierre
Alfred van der Essen

CHILE

Representatives
His Excellency
Marcial Mora
(Head of Delegation)
His Excellency
Enrique Gajardo
His Excellency
Julio Escudero
Alternate Representative
Horacio Suarez

THE FRENCH REPUBLIC

Representative
His Excellency
Pierre Charpentier
(Head of Delegation)
Alternate Representative
Guy Scalabre

JAPAN

Representatives
His Excellency
Koichiro Asakai
(Head of Delegation)
Takeso Shimoda

NEW ZEALAND

Representatives
The Right Honorable
Walter Nash, C.H.
(Head of Delegation)
A. D. McIntosh, C.M.G.
(Deputy Head of Delegation)
Alternate Representative
G. D. L. White, M.V.O.

NORWAY

Representatives
His Excellency
Paul Koht
(Head of Delegation)
Torfinn Oftedal
(Deputy Head of Delegation)
Alternate Representatives
Dr. Anders K. Orvin
Gunnar Haerum

UNION OF SOUTH AFRICA

Representatives

The Honorable
Eric H. Louw
(Head of Delegation)
His Excellency
W. C. du Plessis
(Deputy Head of Delegation)

Alternate Representatives

J. G. Stewart
A. G. Dunn
D. Stuart Franklin

UNION OF SOVIET SOCIALIST REPUBLICS

Representatives

His Excellency
Vasili V. Kuznetsov
(Head of Delegation)
Grigory I. Tunkin

Alternate Representatives

Alexander A. Afanasiev
Vice Admiral Valentin A.
Chekurov
Mikhail M. Somov
Mikhail N. Smirnovsky

UNITED KINGDOM

Representatives

Sir Esler Dening, G.C.M.G.,
O.B.E.
(Head of Delegation)
His Excellency
Sir Harold Caccia, G.C.M.G.,
K.C.V.O.

Alternate Representatives

H. N. Brain, C.M.G., O.B.E.
The Viscount Hood, C.M.G.
The Honorable
H. A. A. Hankey, C.V.O.

UNITED STATES OF AMERICA

Representative

The Honorable
Herman Phleger
(Head of Delegation)

Alternate Representatives

The Honorable
Paul C. Daniels
George H. Owen

The Conference met at Washington on October 15, 1959. It had before it as a basis for discussion working papers considered in the course of informal preparatory talks among representatives of the twelve countries who had met in Washington following the aforesaid invitation of the Government of the United States of America.

At the opening Plenary Session of the Conference the Honorable Herman Phleger, Head of the United States Delegation, was elected Chairman of the Conference. Mr. Henry E. Allen was appointed Secretary General of the Conference and Rapporteur.

The Conference established two Committees under rotating chairmanship to deal with the items on the agenda of the Conference. Following initial consideration of such items, these Committees were reconstituted as a Committee of the Whole. There were also established a Credentials Committee, a Drafting Committee, and a Committee on Style.

The final session of the Conference was held on December 1, 1959.

As a result of the deliberations of the Conference, as recorded in the summary records and reports of the respective Committees and of the

Plenary Sessions, the Conference formulated and submitted for signature on December 1, 1959, the Antarctic Treaty.

The Conference recommended to the participating Governments that they appoint representatives to meet in Washington within two months after the signing of the Treaty and thereafter at such times as may be convenient, pending the entry into force of the Treaty, to consult together and to recommend to their Governments such interim arrangements regarding the matters dealt with in the Treaty as they may deem desirable.

IN WITNESS WHEREOF, the following Plenipotentiaries sign this Final Act.

DONE at Washington this first day of December, one thousand nine hundred and fifty-nine, in the English, French, Russian and Spanish languages, each version being equally authentic, in a single original which shall be deposited in the archives of the Government of the United States of America. The Government of the United States of America shall transmit certified copies thereof to all the other Governments represented at the Conference.

For Argentina:
ADOLFO SCILINGO
F. BELLO

For Australia:
HOWARD BEALE
J. C. G. KEVIN
M. R. BOOKER

For Belgium:
OBERT DE THIEUSIES

For Chile:
MARCIAL MORA M.
E. GAJARDO V.
JULIO ESCUDERO

For the French Republic:
PIERRE CHARPENTIER

For Japan:
KOICHIRO ASAKAI
T. SHIMODA

For New Zealand:
G. D. L. WHITE

For Norway:
PAUL KOHT

For the Union of South Africa:
WENTZEL C. DU PLESSIS

For the Union of Soviet Socialist Republics:
V. KUZNETSOV [Romanization]
G. TUNKIN [Romanization]

For the United Kingdom of Great Britain and Northern Ireland:
HAROLD CACCIA

For the United States of America:
HERMAN PHLEGER
PAUL C. DANIELS

Text of Antarctic Treaty

The Governments of Argentina, Australia, Belgium, Chile, the French Republic, Japan, New Zealand, Norway, the Union of South Africa, the Union of Soviet Socialist Republics, the United Kingdom of Great Britain and Northern Ireland, and the United States of America,

Recognizing that it is in the interest of all mankind that Antarctica shall continue forever to be used exclusively for peaceful purposes and shall not become the scene or object of international discord;

169

Acknowledging the substantial contributions to scientific knowledge resulting from international cooperation in scientific investigation in Antarctica;

Convinced that the establishment of a firm foundation for the continuation and development of such cooperation on the basis of freedom of scientific investigation in Antarctica as applied during the International Geophysical Year accords with the interests of science and the progress of all mankind;

Convinced also that a treaty ensuring the use of Antarctica for peaceful purposes only and the continuance of international harmony in Antarctica will further the purposes and principles embodied in the Charter of the United Nations;

Have agreed as follows:

ARTICLE I

1. Antarctica shall be used for peaceful purposes only. There shall be prohibited, *inter alia,* any measures of a military nature, such as the establishment of military bases and fortifications, the carrying out of military maneuvers, as well as the testing of any type of weapons.

2. The present Treaty shall not prevent the use of military personnel or equipment for scientific research or for any other peaceful purpose.

ARTICLE II

Freedom of scientific investigation in Antarctica and cooperation toward that end, as applied during the International Geophysical Year, shall continue, subject to the provisions of the present Treaty.

ARTICLE III

1. In order to promote international cooperation in scientific investigation in Antarctica, as provided for in Article II of the present Treaty, the Contracting Parties agree that, to the greatest extent feasible and practicable:

(a) information regarding plans for scientific programs in Antarctica shall be exchanged to permit maximum economy and efficiency of operations;

(b) scientific personnel shall be exchanged in Antarctica between expeditions and stations;

(c) scientific observations and results from Antarctica shall be exchanged and made freely available.

2. In implementing this Article, every encouragement shall be given to the establishment of cooperative working relations with those Specialized Agencies of the United Nations and other international organizations having a scientific or technical interest in Antarctica.

ARTICLE IV

1. Nothing contained in the present Treaty shall be interpreted as:

(a) a renunciation by any Contracting Party of previously asserted rights of or claims to territorial sovereignty in Antarctica;

(b) a renunciation or diminution by any Contracting Party of any basis of claim to territorial sovereignty in Antarctica which it may have whether as a result of its activities or those of its nationals in Antarctica, or otherwise;

(c) prejudicing the position of any Contracting Party as regards its recognition or non-recognition of any other State's right of or claim or basis of claim to territorial sovereignty in Antarctica.

2. No acts or activities taking place while the present Treaty is in force shall constitute a basis for asserting, supporting or denying a claim to territorial sovereignty in Antarctica or create any rights of sovereignty in Antarctica. No new claim, or enlargement of an existing claim, to territorial sovereignty in Antarctica shall be asserted while the present Treaty is in force.

ARTICLE V

1. Any nuclear explosions in Antarctica and the disposal there of radioactive waste material shall be prohibited.

2. In the event of the conclusion of international agreements concerning the use of nuclear energy, including nuclear explosions and the disposal of radioactive waste material, to which all of the Contracting Parties whose representatives are entitled to participate in the meetings provided for under Article IX are parties, the rules established under such agreements shall apply in Antarctica.

ARTICLE VI

The provisions of the present Treaty shall apply to the area south of 60° South Latitude, including all ice shelves, but nothing in the present Treaty shall prejudice or in any way affect the rights, or the exercise of the rights, of any State under international law with regard to the high seas within that area.

ARTICLE VII

1. In order to promote the objectives and ensure the observance of the provisions of the present Treaty, each Contracting Party whose representatives are entitled to participate in the meetings referred to in Article IX of the Treaty shall have the right to designate observers to carry out any inspection provided for by the present Article. Observers shall be nationals of the Contracting Parties which designate them. The names of observers shall be communicated to every other Contracting Party having the right to designate observers, and like notice shall be given of the termination of their appointment.

2. Each observer designated in accordance with the provisions of paragraph 1 of this Article shall have complete freedom of access at any time to any or all areas of Antarctica.

3. All areas of Antarctica, including all stations, installations and equipment within those areas, and all ships and aircraft at points of discharging or embarking cargoes or personnel in Antarctica, shall be open at all times to inspection by any observers designated in accordance with paragraph 1 of this Article.

4. Aerial observation may be carried out at any time over any or all areas of Antarctica by any of the Contracting Parties having the right to designate observers.

5. Each Contracting Party shall, at the time when the present Treaty enters into force for it, inform the other Contracting Parties, and thereafter shall give them notice in advance, of

(a) all expeditions to and within Antarctica, on the part of its ships or nationals, and all expeditions to Antarctica organized in or proceeding from its territory;

(b) all stations in Antarctica occupied by its nationals; and

(c) any military personnel or equipment intended to be introduced by it into Antarctica subject to the conditions prescribed in paragraph 2 of Article I of the present Treaty.

ARTICLE VIII

1. In order to facilitate the exercise of their functions under the present Treaty, and without prejudice to the respective positions of the Contracting Parties relating to jurisdiction over all other persons in Antarctica, observers designated under paragraph 1 of Article VII and scientific personnel exchanged under subparagraph 1(b) of Article III of the Treaty, and members of the staffs accompanying any such persons, shall be subject only to the jurisdiction of the Contracting Party of which they are nationals in respect of all acts or omissions occurring while they are in Antarctica for the purpose of exercising their functions.

2. Without prejudice to the provisions of paragraph 1 of this Article, and pending the adoption of measures in pursuance of subparagraph 1(e) of Article IX, the Contracting Parties concerned in any case of dispute with regard to the exercise of jurisdiction in Antarctica shall immediately consult together with a view to reaching a mutually acceptable solution.

ARTICLE IX

1. Representatives of the Contracting Parties named in the preamble to the present Treaty shall meet at the City of Canberra within two months after the date of entry into force of the Treaty, and thereafter at suitable intervals and places, for the purpose of exchanging information, consulting together on matters of common interest pertaining to Antarctica, and formulating and considering, and recommending to their Governments, measures in furtherance of the principles and objectives of the Treaty, including measures regarding:

(a) use of Antarctica for peaceful purposes only;

(b) facilitation of scientific research in Antarctica;

(c) facilitation of international scientific cooperation in Antarctica;

(d) facilitation of the exercise of the rights of inspection provided for in Article VII of the Treaty;

(e) questions relating to the exercise of jurisdiction in Antarctica;

(f) preservation and conservation of living resources in Antarctica.

2. Each Contracting Party which has become a party to the present Treaty by accession under Article XIII shall be entitled to appoint representatives to participate in the meetings referred to in paragraph 1 of the present Article, during such time as that Contracting Party demonstrates its interest in Antarctica by conducting substantial scientific research activity there, such as the establishment of a scientific station or the despatch of a scientific expedition.

3. Reports from the observers referred to in Article VII of the present Treaty shall be transmitted to the representatives of the Contracting Parties participating in the meetings referred to in paragraph 1 of the present Article.

4. The measures referred to in paragraph 1 of this Article shall become effective when approved by all the Contracting Parties whose representatives were entitled to participate in the meetings held to consider those measures.

5. Any or all of the rights established in the present Treaty may be exercised as from the date of entry into force of the Treaty whether or not any measures facilitating the exercise of such rights have been proposed, considered or approved as provided in this Article.

Article X

Each of the Contracting Parties undertakes to exert appropriate efforts, consistent with the Charter of the United Nations, to the end that no one engages in any activity in Antarctica contrary to the principles or purposes of the present Treaty.

Article XI

1. If any dispute arises between two or more of the Contracting Parties concerning the interpretation or application of the present Treaty, those Contracting Parties shall consult among themselves with a view to having the dispute resolved by negotiation, inquiry, mediation, conciliation, arbitration, judicial settlement or other peaceful means of their own choice.

2. Any dispute of this character not so resolved shall, with the consent, in each case, of all parties to the dispute, be referred to the International Court of Justice for settlement; but failure to reach agreement on reference to the International Court shall not absolve parties to the dispute from the responsibility of continuing to seek to resolve it by any of the various peaceful means referred to in paragraph 1 of this Article.

Article XII

1. (a) The present Treaty may be modified or amended at any time by unanimous agreement of the Contracting Parties whose representatives are entitled to participate in the meetings provided for under Article IX. Any such modification or amendment shall enter into force when the depositary Government has received notice from all such Contracting Parties that they have ratified it.

(b) Such modification or amendment shall thereafter enter into force as to any other Contracting Party when notice of ratification by it has been received by the depositary Government. Any such Contracting Party from which no notice of ratification is received within a period of two years from the date of entry into force of the modification or amendment in accordance with the provisions of subparagraph 1(a) of this Article shall be deemed to have withdrawn from the present Treaty on the date of the expiration of such period.

2. (a) If after the expiration of thirty years from the date of entry into force of the present Treaty, any of the Contracting Parties whose representatives are entitled to participate in the meetings provided for under Article IX so requests by a communication addressed to the depositary Government, a Conference of all the Contracting Parties shall be held as soon as practicable to review the operation of the Treaty.

(b) Any modification or amendment to the present Treaty which is approved at such a Conference by a majority of the Contracting Parties there represented, including a majority of those whose representatives are entitled to participate in the meetings provided for under Article IX, shall be communicated by the depositary Government to all the Contracting Parties immediately after the termination of the Conference and shall enter into force in accordance with the provisions of paragraph 1 of the present Article.

(c) If any such modification or amendment has not entered into force in accordance with the provisions of subparagraph 1(a) of this Article within a period of two years after the date of its communication to all the Contracting Parties, any Contracting Party may at any time after the expiration of that period give notice to the depositary Government of its withdrawal from the present Treaty; and such withdrawal shall take effect two years after the receipt of the notice by the depositary Government.

Article XIII

1. The present Treaty shall be subject to ratification by the signatory States. It shall be open for accession by any State which is a Member of the United Nations, or by any other State which may be invited to accede to the Treaty with the consent of all the Contracting Parties whose representatives are entitled to participate in the meetings provided for under Article IX of the Treaty.

2. Ratification of or accession to the present Treaty shall be effected by each State in accordance with its constitutional processes.

174

3. Instruments of ratification and instruments of accession shall be deposited with the Government of the United States of America, hereby designated as the depositary Government.

4. The depositary Government shall inform all signatory and acceding States of the date of each deposit of an instrument of ratification or accession, and the date of entry into force of the Treaty and of any modification or amendment thereto.

5. Upon the deposit of instruments of ratification by all the signatory States, the present Treaty shall enter into force for those States and for States which have deposited instruments of accession. Thereafter the Treaty shall enter into force for any acceding State upon the deposit of its instrument of accession.

6. The present Treaty shall be registered by the depositary Government pursuant to Article 102 of the Charter of the United Nations.

ARTICLE XIV

The present Treaty, done in the English, French, Russian, and Spanish languages, each version being equally authentic, shall be deposited in the archives of the Government of the United States of America, which shall transmit duly certified copies thereof to the Governments of the signatory and acceding States.

IN WITNESS WHEREOF, the undersigned Plenipotentiaries, duly authorized, have signed the present Treaty.

DONE at Washington this first day of December, one thousand nine hundred and fifty-nine.

For Argentina:
ADOLFO SCILINGO
F. BELLO

For Australia:
HOWARD BEALE

For Belgium:
OBERT DE THIEUSIES

For Chile:
MARCIAL MORA M.
E. GAJARDO V.
JULIO ESCUDERO

For the French Republic:
PIERRE CHARPENTIER

For Japan:
KOICHIRO ASAKAI
T. SHIMODA

For New Zealand:
G. D. L. WHITE

For Norway:
PAUL KOHT

For the Union of South Africa:
WENTZEL C. DU PLESSIS

For the Union of Soviet Socialist Republics:
V. KUZNETSOV [Romanization]

For the United Kingdom of Great Britain and Northern Ireland:
HAROLD CACCIA

For the United States of America:
HERMAN PHLEGER
PAUL C. DANIELS

2

Notes on Antarctic Place Names

THERE was a time when an explorer could name a geographic feature almost anything he cared to. Sir James Clark Ross named the volcano on Ross Island Mt. Erebus, after his ship, in 1841. The island was, in turn, named after Sir James by Robert Scott in 1902. Charcot named a mountain after Scott around 1908, and Nordenskjöld named a bay after Charcot in 1901, before Charcot had even become interested in the Antarctic. In 1909, Edwin Balch named a coast after Nordenskjöld, and Charcot named a mountain after Balch around 1909. Coasts, mountains, bays, ice-shelves, glaciers, ranges, islands, spits, islets, sounds, and points are all named quite arbitrarily, after wives, sweethearts, ships, dogs, friends, relatives, patrons, societies, and general impressions. Obviously, it had to stop somewhere!

There now exists a U.S. Board on Geographic Names, and all names must pass the approval of this body. There are hard and fast rules that govern the assignment of names. The first problem is the identification of a feature. We must remember that some features have been seen only two or three times in history and often badly misplaced on the map. A mountain may have been seen from the West in 1880 and called Smith Mountain, and then seen from the East in 1920 and called Jones Mountain. In neither case was it necessarily properly located, and in 1942 it may have been seen from the air and called Pelican Peak. This kind of error is no longer likely to occur. After painstaking research has established precedence, the feature is given the name that honestly belongs to it. New features are no longer named after wives and sweethearts, but after men who figure well in Antarctic exploration. Non-personal names (events, ships, organizations, etc.), can still be used if really appropriate. The problem is huge and the task formidable, but order seems to be coming out of chaos.

In this book, we have adhered to the decisions of the U.S. Board on Geographic Names. If anyone seriously intends to study the Antarctic further, there is a book—*Geographic Names of Antarctica* (Gazetteer No. 14), 1956—available from the Superintendent of Documents, Washington 25, D.C., for $2.25. It contains 332 pages and offers a wealth of invaluable information. We most earnestly commend it to your attention.

3

List of Antarctic Expeditions from 1675 to 1955

FOR quick reference, this list supplies basic details of 161 known expeditions south of the Antarctic Circle. This list is not complete. Indeed, it certainly couldn't be. Not every ship that crossed into the Antarctic Ocean in pursuit of the whale and the fur seal, left records where we can find them. Some of these ships were lost, and no records exist. Ships that sailed into Antarctic waters on political or military errands and did not add to our knowledge of the area are not included.

Before 1675, the record is decidedly blurred. We have talked about Piri Reis's map and the impression it gives that a dry, warm Antarctic continent was known to man at the dawn of recorded history. Other maps exist which also confuse the issue.

We can't very well list unnamed ships, with unknown captains performing unknown feats in years not recorded. We will start with 1675 and list those expeditions whose records seem clear and authentic. Our authority is the Office of Geography, Department of the Interior, and their publication, *Geographic Names of Antarctica*. The list was compiled by Kenneth J. Bertrand and Fred G. Alberts. It is reproduced by permission.

Years	Country of Origin	Leaders	Ships	Remarks
1675	Great Britain	Antonio de La Roche	Unknown	Accidental. Storm driven. South Georgia.
1738–39	France	J. B. C. Bouvet de Lozier	Aigle and Marie	Discovered Bouvet Island.
1756	Spain	Unknown	Leon	South Georgia.
1772–75	Great Britain	James Cook	Resolution and Adventure	Circumnavigation south of 50° S.
1800	United States	Various	Various	Sealing. Scant records.
1808	Great Britain	James Linsay, Thomas Hopper	Snow Swan and Otter	Whaling.
1819	Great Britain	William Smith	Williams	Commercial voyage.
1819–20	Argentina	Carlos Timblon	San Juan and Nepomuceno	Sealing.
1819–20	Great Britain	Unknown	Espirito Santo	Sealing.
1819–20	United States	James Sheffield	Hersilia	Sealing.
1819–20	Great Britain	Edward Bransfield	Williams	South Shetlands.
1819–20	Russia	Thaddeus Bellingshausen	Vostok and Mirny	Scientific. Circumnavigated mostly south of 60° S.
1820–21	United States	Benjamin Pendleton, Nathaniel Palmer	Frederick, Hersilia, Express, Free Gift, Hero	Probable first sighting of mainland of the Antarctic (Palmer).
1820–21	Great Britain	Richard Sherratt	Lady Trowbridge	Sealing. Ship lost.
1820–21	United States	John Davis, Chris. Burdick	Huron, Huntress, Cecilia	Cecilia landed probable first party on mainland of Antarctic. Sealing expedition.
1820–21	Great Britain	Clark	Lord-Melville	Probable first wintering.
1820–21	United States	Charles Barnard	Charity, Aurora, Jane Maria, Henry	Sealing.
1820–21	Great Britain	James Weddell	Janey, Eliza	Sealing.
1820–21	United States	Thomas Ray	Harmony, William & Mary	Sealing.
1820–21	United States	Jonathan Winship	O'Cain, Stranger	Sealing.
1820–21	United States	Alexander Clark	Clothier, Emiline, Catherine	Sealing. Clothier lost.
1820–21	United States	William Orne	General Knox, Nancy and Governor-Brooks	Sealing.
1820–21	Great Britain	William Smith	Williams	Sealing.
1820–21	Great Britain	Robert Fildes	Unknown	Sealing.
1820–21	Great Britain	McFarlane	Dragon	Sealing.

Years	Country of Origin	Leaders	Ships	Remarks
1820–21	Great Britain	George Powell	Dove	Sealing. Combined with Nathaniel Palmer. Some mapmaking of note.
1821–22	United States	Benjamin Pendleton, Nathaniel Palmer	Frederick, Alabama Packet, Express, Free Gift, James Monroe, Hero	Sealing. Some exploration
1821–22	United States	John Davis	Huron, Cecilia	Sealing
1821–22	Great Britain	James Weddell	Jane	Sealing.
1821–22	United States	Benjamin Morrell, Robert Johnson	Wasp, Jane Maria	Sealing.
1822–23	United States	Benjamin Morrell	Wasp	Sealing.
1822–24	Great Britain	James Weddell, Mathew Brisbane	Jane, Beaufoy	Sealing and charting
1824–25	Great Britain	Edward Hughes	Sprightly	Sealing. Some charting
1828–31	Great Britain	Henry Foster, RN	Chanticleer	Government scientific expedition
1829–31	United States	Benjamin Pendleton	Seraph, Annawan, Penguin	Sealing and scientific.
1829–31	United States	James Brown	Pacific	Sealing
1830–32	Great Britain	John Biscoe	Tula, Lively	Circumnavigation
1831	Australia	Samuel Harvey	Venus	Sealing and whaling, penetrated to Ross Sea.
1833–34	Great Britain	Henry Rea	Hopeful, Rose	Exploration. Hopeful crushed by ice
1833–34	Great Britain	Peter Kemp	Magnet	Exploration
1837–40	France	Dumont D'Urville	Astrolabe, Zelee	Exploration
1839	Great Britain	John Balleny	Eliza-Scott, Sabrina	Exploration
1839–42	United States	Charles Wilkes	Vincennes, Peacock, Porpoise, Sea Gull, Flying Fish, Relief	Exploration. Established continental proportions of Antarctic land mass
1839–43	Great Britain	James C. Ross	Erebus, Terror	Exploration
1841–42	United States	William Smyley	Ohio	Sealing and exploration
1845	Great Britain	T. E. L. Moore	Pagoda	Magnetic observations
1853–54	United States	John Heard	Oriental	
1853–54	Great Britain	McDonald	Samarang	
1855–56	United States	Erasmus Darwin, Rogers & Franklin Smith	Corinthian, Laurens, Atlas, Exile, Franklin, Mechanic	Sealing and mapping
1857	United States	Henry Rogers	Zoe	Sealing
1873–74	Germany	Edward Dallmann	Grönland	Sealing and exploration
1874	Great Britain	George Nares, Wyville Thomson	Challenger	Exploration and oceanography

180

Years	Country of Origin	Leaders	Ships	Remarks
1874	Germany	Von Reibnitz	*Arrona*	Exploration
1882–83	Germany	K. Schrader	*Moltke, Marie*	Scientific and exploration
1892–93	Scotland	A. Fairweather, R. Davidson, T. Robertson, J. Davidson	*Balaena, Diana, Active, Polar Star*	Whaling and exploration
1892–93	Norway	C. A. Larsen	*Jason*	Whaling, sealing, and exploration
1893–94	Norway	C. A. Larsen	*Jason, Hertha, Castor*	Sealing and exploration
1894–95	Norway	L. Kristensen, H. S. Bull	*Antarctic*	Sealing and exploration
1897–99	Belgium	Adrien de Gerlache	*Belgica*	Exploration and science
1898	Germany	Karlchun	*Valdivia*	Oceanographic
1898–1900	Great Britain	C. Borchgrevink	*Southern Cross*	Exploration and science
1901–03	Germany	E. Von Drygalski	*Gauss*	Scientific
1901–04	Sweden	O. Nordenskjöld	*Antarctic*	Exploration. Ship crushed by ice
1901–04	Great Britain	R. F. Scott	*Discovery*	Exploration
1902–03	Great Britain	Wm. Colbeck	*Morning*	Partial relief for Scott expedition of 1901–1904
1902–04	Scotland	William Bruce	*Scotia*	Exploration
1903	Argentina	J. Irizar	*Uruguay*	Relief of Swedish expedition of 1901–1904
1903–04	Great Britain	William Colbeck	*Morning, Terra Nova*	Partial relief of Scott expedition of 1901–1904
1903–05	France	J. Charcot	*Francais*	Exploration
1904	Argentina	Ismael Galindes	*Uruguay*	Set up meteorological station. Still in operation. Relieved annually
1904–05	Norway & Argentina	C. Larsen	*Fortuna, Louisa, Rolf, Guardia Nacional*	Whaling
1905–06	Norway	A. Lange	*Admiralen*	Whaling. First factory ship
1906	Great Britain	M. H. Hodges	*Sappho*	Whaling investigation
1907–09	Great Britain	E. Shackleton	*Nimrod*	Exploration to within 97 miles of Pole
1908–10	France	J. Charcot	*Pourquoi-Pas?*	Exploration
1910	Great Britain	Unknown	*Wakefield*	Searched for survivors of Australian liner; also hydrographic

Years	Country of Origin	Leaders	Ships	Remarks
1910	Great Britain, Norway	A. Evensen	*Mangoro*	Sealing
1910–12	Norway	R. Amundsen	*Fram*	Scientific, exploration. Reached Pole 12/14/11
1910–13	Great Britain	R. F. Scott	*Terra Nova*	Scientific, exploration. Reached Pole 1/17/12. Scott and 4 others lost
1911–12	Japan	Choku Shirase	*Kainan Maru*	Exploration
1911–12	Germany	W. Filchner	*Deutschland*	Exploration. Ship caught in ice for 9 months
1911–12	Norway	O. Jorgensen	*Thulla*	Experimental whaling
1911–14	Australia	D. Mawson	*Aurora*	Advanced exploration and scientific. Fatalities
1912–13	Norway	P. Sorlle	*Palmer*	Whaling and charting
1912–13	United States	B. D. Cleveland, R. C. Murphy	*Daisy*	Whaling, sealing, charting, scientific
1913–14	Norway	H. Borge	*Polynesia*	Whaling and charting
1914–16	Great Britain	E. Shackleton	*Endurance, Aurora*	Exploration. *Endurance* crushed in ice
1920	Great Britain	H. Hope	*Dartmouth*	Exploration
1921–22	Great Britain	J. Cope	Various whaling vessels	Exploration and scientific
1921–22	Great Britain	E. Shackleton, F. Wild	*Quest*	Exploration and scientific. Shackleton died
1923–24	Norway	C. Larsen	*Sir James, Clark Ross, Star I,* plus four other whale catchers	First whaling in Ross Sea
1923–24	Great Britain	S. Beckmann, G. Mathisen	*Sevilla, Roald Amundsen,* plus whale catchers	Whaling
1924–25	Norway	C. Larsen	*Sir James, Clark Ross* & whale catchers	Whaling. Captain Larsen died
1925	Great Britain	N. Mackintosh		Scientific station set upon S. Georgia. In operation until 1931 ("*Discovery Investigations*")
1925–26	Great Britain	S. Kemp	*Discovery*	Biology, Hydrography ("*Discovery Investigations*")
1925–26	Germany	A. Merz	*Meteor*	Oceanography
1926–27	Great Britain	S. Kemp	*Discovery, William Scoresby*	Whaling study ("*Discovery Investigations*")
1927	Norway	E. Tofte	*Odd I*	Exploration
1927–28	Norway	H. Horntvedt	*Norvegia*	Oceanography
1927–28	Norway	Ola Olstad, O. Holtedahl	Various whaling ships	Biology and geology

| --- | --- | --- | --- | --- |
1928–29	Germany	L. Kohl-Larsen	Various whaling ships	Charting and glaciology
1928–29	France	A. Delarue	Austral	Geology
1928–29	Great Britain & United States	Hubert Wilkins	Hektoria	Exploration. First Antarctic flights
1928–29	Norway	N. Larsen	Norvegia	Exploration
1928–30	United States	R. E. Byrd	City of New York, Eleanor Bolling	Exploration. First flight to Pole. One plane lost
1929–30	Great Britain & United States	H. Wilkins	Whaling ships & William Scoresby	Exploration. Planes used for third time
1929–30	Norway	H. Riiser-Larsen	Norvegia	Exploration, scientific, aviation
1929–31	Great Britain, Australia, New Zealand	D. Mawson	Discovery	Scientific, exploration, charting, aviation
1929–31	Great Britain	S. Kemp	Discovery II	Oceanography. ("Discovery Investigations")
1930–31	Norway	G. Isachsen, H. Riiser-Larsen	Norvegia, Thorshavn	Scientific, exploration
1930–31	Norway	Various	Various whaling	Whaling
1930–31	Norway	O. Borchgrevink	Antarctic	Whaling and charting
1930–31	Norway	H. Halvorsen	Sevilla	Whaling and charting
1931	Norway	L. Christensen	Thorshavn	Refueling of whaling fleet, charting
1931–33	Great Britain	D. John	Discovery II	Oceanography ("Discovery Investigations")
1932–33	Norway	L. Christensen	Thorshavn	Refueling of whaling fleet. Meteorology
1932–33	Norway	H. Riiser-Larsen	Various whaling	Exploration
1933–34	Norway	L. Christensen	Thorshavn	Exploration, meteorology, and hydrography
1933–34	United States	L. Ellsworth	Wyatt Earp	Aviation. Plane lost
1933–35	Great Britain	N. Mackintosh	Discovery II	Oceanography, exploration ("Discovery Investigations")
1933–35	United States	R. E. Byrd	Bear of Oakland, Jacob Ruppert	Exploration. Full scientific, extensive aviation
1934–35	Norway	K. Mikkelsen	Thorshavn	Refueling whaling fleet, exploration
1934–35	United States	L. Ellsworth	Wyatt Earp	Aviation. Failure. Some exploration
1934–37	Great Britain	J. Rymill	Penola	Extensive exploration. Aviation
1935–36	United States	L. Ellsworth	Wyatt Earp	Exploratory aviation

Years	Country of Origin	Leaders	Ships	Remarks
1935–36	Great Britain	G. Rayner	*William Scoresby*	Whale marking (*"Discovery Investigations"*)
1935–37	Great Britain	G. Deacon	*Discovery II*	(*"Discovery Investigations"*)
1936–37	Norway	L. Christensen	*Thorsham, Firern*	Aerial survey
1937–38	Great Britain	G. Rayner	*William Scoresby*	Whale marking (*"Discovery Investigations"*)
1937–39	Great Britain	N. Mackintosh, H. Herdman	*Discovery II*	Scientific (*"Discovery Investigations"*)
1938–39	United States	L. Ellsworth	*Wyatt Earp*	Aviation exploration
1938–39	Germany	A. Ritscher	*Schwabenland*	Scientific—aerial survey. Political purposes
1939–41	United States	R. E. Byrd	*Bear, North Star*	Extensive exploration, scientific obervations, and aerial survey
1942	Argentina	A. Oddera	*Primero-De-Mayo*	Survey and territorial claim to Deception Island
1943	Argentina	S. Harriague	*Primero-De-Mayo*	Survey
1943–45	Great Britain	J. W. Marr	*William Scoresby, Fitzroy*	Falkland Islands Dependencies survey, full scientific (OPERATION TABARIN)
1945–46	Great Britain	A. Taylor	*William Scoresby, Fitzroy, Eagle*	Falkland Islands Dependencies survey, full scientific
1946–47	Great Britain	E. Bingham	*William Scoresby, Fitzroy, Trepassey*	Falkland Islands Dependencies survey, full scientific
1946–47	Great Britain	R. Trouton, R. Pedersen, J. Grierson	*Balaena*	Whaling. Aerial spotting used, scientific
1946–47	Great Britain	N. Rankin	*Albatross*	Wildlife photography. PRIVATE
1946–47	United States	R. E. Byrd, R. H. Cruzen, G. Dufer, E. Bond	13 ships of *Task Force 68: Mt. Olympus, Yancey, Merrick, Northwind, Sennet, Philippine Sea, Burton Island, Pine Island, Brownson, Canisteo, Currituck, Henderson, Cacapon*	Aerial test, equipment test, training, scientific, exploratory ("Operation Highjump"), U.S.N.
1947	Argentina	L. Garcia	*King, Murature, Ministro Ezcurra, Don Samuel, Granville, Patagonia, Chaco, Fournier*	Political purposes. Survey, lighthouse construction
1947	Chile	F. G. Toro	*Iquique, Angamos*	Base construction

Years	Country of Origin	Leaders	Ships	Remarks
1947–48	Argentina	R. Hermelo	Bouchard, Granville, King, Pampa, Ministro Ezcurra, Murature, Chiriguano, Santa Viron, Seaver, Parker, Esv Brunt, Charrua	Base construction, naval maneuvers, aerial survey
1947–48	United States	G. Ketchum	Edisto, Burton Island	U.S.N. "Operation Windmill." Ground control data for aerial photography
1947–48	Norway	N. Larsen	Brategg	Oceanography, geology, zoology
1947–48	United States	F. Ronne	Port of Beaumont, Texas	Full and extensive scientific
1947–48	Great Britain	K. Butler	Fitzroy, Trepassey	Falkland Islands Dependencies survey. Full scientific, cooperation with Ronne
1947–48	Chile	E. Navarette	Covadonga, Rancagua, Presidente-Pinto	Base construction and maintenance
1947–55	Australia	S. Campbell, P. Law	Wyatt Earp, Labuan, Tottan, Kista Dan	Full and extensive exploration, survey. Scientific
1948–49	Great Britain	V. Fuchs	John Biscoe	Falkland Islands Dependencies survey. One base burned, killing 2 men; full program
1948–49	Argentina	Unknown	Pampa, Sanaviron, Chaco	General survey
1948–49	Chile	L. Fontaine	Covadonga, Maipo, Lautaro	Station relief
1948–53	France	A. Liotard, M. Barre, M. Marret	Commandant-Charcot, Totton	Extensive scientific and exploration
1949–52	Norway, Great Britain, Sweden	J. Giaever	Norsel	Full-scale program, 3 men lost
1949–53	Great Britain	V. Fuchs	John Biscoe, Sparrow, Snipe, Burghead Bay	Falkland Islands Dependencies survey. Full scientific schedule
1950–51	Great Britain	H. F. P. Herdman	Discovery II	Oceanographic
1951–52	Great Britain	V. D. Carse	Southern Opal, Stina, Skua	PRIVATE. Scientific
1953–54	Great Britain	V. D. Carse	Polar Maid, Albatross, Southern Opal	PRIVATE. Scientific
1954–55	Argentina	L. R. Capurro	General-San-Martin	Scientific, exploratory
1954–55	United States	G. Jacobsen	Atka	Pre-IGY survey

Summary of the Expeditions Listed in Appendix 3

TOTAL NUMBER: 161
BY COUNTRY *

Argentina	10 †
Australia	4
Belgium	1
Chile	3 †
France	6
Germany	8 ‡
Great Britain	65 †
Japan	1
New Zealand	1
Norway	29
Russia	1
Scotland	2
Spain	1
Sweden	2
United States of America	34

All of the 12 nations participating in the IGY Antarctic program, except one, the Union of South Africa, appear on the above list, indicating an interest in the area pre-dating the IGY. Of the 15 nations listed, only 4—Spain, Germany, Scotland, and Sweden—did not participate in the IGY Antarctic program. The continuity of interest is obvious.

* Expeditions sponsored by more than one country are repeated statistics.

† Argentina, Chile, and Great Britain have been involved in an often bitter controversy over claims in the South Atlantic. A number of "political" voyages took place which are not included.

‡ Does not include World War II military missions.

EXPEDITIONS BY HALF-CENTURY:

1700–1750	1
1751–1800	2
1801–1850	41
1851–1900	15
1901–1950	96

NUMBER OF KNOWN SEALING EXPEDITIONS OF THE 161: 35+
NUMBER OF KNOWN WHALING EXPEDITIONS OF THE 161: 31 *

* Does not include whaling activities of the last two decades, which have been extensive.

APPROXIMATE NUMBER OF KNOWN SHIPS INVOLVED: 244
EXPEDITIONS BY YEAR (LISTED BY EXPEDITION START-YEAR ONLY):

Year		Year		Year	
1675...	1	1882...	1	1927...	3
1738...	1	1892...	2	1928...	5
1756...	1	1893...	1	1929...	4
1772...	1	1894...	1	1930...	4
1800...	1	1897...	1	1931...	2
1808...	1	1898...	2	1932...	2
1819...	6 *	1901...	3	1933...	4
1820...	14 *	1902...	2	1934...	3
1821...	4 *	1903...	3	1935...	3
1822...	2	1904...	2	1936...	1
1824...	1	1905...	1	1937...	2
1828...	1	1906...	1	1938...	2
1829...	2	1907...	1	1939...	1
1830...	1	1908...	1	1942...	1
1831...	1	1910...	4	1943...	2
1833...	2	1911...	4	1945...	1
1837...	1	1912...	2	1946...	4
1839...	3	1913...	1	1947...	9
1841...	1	1914...	1	1948...	4
1845...	1	1920...	1	1949...	2
1853...	2	1921...	2	1950...	1
1855...	1	1923...	2	1951...	1
1857...	1	1924...	1	1953...	1
1873...	1	1925...	3	1954...	2
1874...	2	1926...	1	†	

* Period of maximum sealing activity.

† Since 1954, the Antarctic has been "inhabited" 12 months of the year. Now that aircraft reach the ice from New Zealand, the number of "craft arrivals" is in the hundreds each year.

4

Antarctic Philately

ONE of the most intriguing specialties to attract stamp collectors in recent years has been Polar philately. A regular journal entitled *Ice Cap News* is published by the American Society of Polar Philatelists. The editor is John J. Herguth, 729 First Street, Westfield, New Jersey. *The Polar News,* published twice a year by the American Polar Society (in care of August Howard, 98-20 62nd Drive, Rego Park 74, New York), has a page or two of news for stamp collectors in each issue.

Collecting Antarctic material falls into three general categories: stamps about Antarctica, stamps issued for Antarctic zones, and Antarctic covers (envelopes)—viz., letters and cards mailed during Antarctic voyages and expeditions.

In the first category are a number of stamps of great interest.

The accompanying table is not complete but it does give a sampling of the kind of subject matter of Antarctic interest that has appeared.

In the second category is a growing number of stamps issued for use in Antarctic and sub-Antarctic regions. Australia has a whole set for "Australian Antarctic Territory." This set features explorers, maps, events, penguins, and equipment. The Falkland Islands, of course, have long issued stamps, many of which include Antarctic

Country	Year	Subject
Argentina............	1947	Four stamps showing Argentinian claim to area of Antarctica claimed by Great Britain
	1951	Four stamps showing Argentinian claim to area of Antarctica claimed by Great Britain
	1953	The rescue ship *Uruguay*—50th anniversary of the rescue by Argentina of the 1901–1904 Swedish expedition
	1954	Planting the Argentine flag in the Antarctic—50th anniversary
	1957	Antarctic claim—map
	1958	IGY issue—map of Antarctica
Australia.............	1954	Flora and fauna map of Antarctica
Belgium..............	1947	Explorer Adrien de Gerlache
	1947	The *Belgica* in the Antarctic—1897
	1957	Sled-dogs and camp
Chile................	1947	Antarctic claim-map
	1958	(Four stamps) Antarctic claim-map
	1958	1588 Antarctic map
Hungary..............	1959	IGY issue: penguins, icebergs, Aurora, snow vehicle, map, and helicopter
Japan................	1957	Map, penguin, and research ship
	1960	Explorer Choku Shirase
Norway..............	1957	Map of Queen Maud Land
	1961	2: Amundsen and the "FRAM" and Amundsen's party at the South Pole
Russia................	1956	Mirny Base
	1959	Glacier survey and Antarctic map, bases, plane, and penguin
Union of South Africa...	1959	Map-honoring expedition
United States of America	1934	Byrd Antarctic Expedition Issue II—map

subjects, whales, penguins, expedition ships, to name a few. The Falkland Islands Dependencies issues are of great interest. Featured are maps, special overprints for an expedition, and a beautiful set of 15 stamps, each one of which bears a picture of a different Antarctic ship, famous in the history of exploration. France has issued more than 24 stamps for her "French Southern and Antarctic Territories." Sea elephants, seals, penguins, skuas, gulls, Sea-leopards, albatrosses, cormorants, explorers, ships, and maps are all pictured in this series.

Still in the second category, New Zealand has issued a set of 4 stamps for use in the Ross Dependency she claims. Shackleton, Scott, Mt. Erebus, H.M.S. *Erebus,* and a map are featured.

Most interesting of the three categories is the collection of mail or covers used on expeditions. Many of the expeditions since 1900, just about all of the important ones, have prepared special envelopes or, at least, special postmarks or cachets. These are colorful, informative, and frequently quite valuable. There are several pamphlets and catalogues in a number of languages which deal with this specialty alone.

Perhaps no branch of stamp collecting, except North Pole philately, is as exciting and rewarding as this new, increasingly popular specialty. It is thrilling, indeed, to hold an envelope in your hand bearing a description of the conditions under which it was "mailed," interesting postmarks and cachets telling of the expedition involved, and carrying with it just a bit of the thrill and drama of Antarctic exploration.

Most modern expeditions are very cooperative about taking special philatelic mail with them to service collectors. The first of the two journals mentioned at the beginning of this Appendix carries information on how to prepare mail to accompany new expeditions and when and where to send it. These envelopes and special cards already exist in bewildering quantity. It is a fascinating hobby that is a constant lesson in history and an endless source of joy to retired explorer and armchair expedition leader alike. The American Topical Association, at 3306 North 50th Street, Milwaukee 16, Wisconsin, is a good place to get further information.

5

Notes on Antarctic Photography

Iᴛ is a rare visitor to the ice who doesn't have the seemingly uncontrollable urge to shoot miles of film. Photography, like everything else at extreme temperatures, becomes something of a problem. Enough photography has been done, however, to permit the evolution of a system. For the shutterbugs who may be interested, here are a few of the problems and some suggested solutions.

THE WINTERIZED CAMERA

Find 10 men who have attempted photography in the Antarctic, and you will almost certainly find 5 who will say that you absolutely must winterize your cameras and 5 who will tell you it isn't necessary. I encountered this split decision before I went down and took two cameras with me, one of which I had winterized. Both cameras worked well to about 20° *below zero,* and then both froze up from time to time. The difference was, the winterized camera thawed out each time without difficulty, and the unwinterized camera groaned pitifully at 47° below, and had to go back to the factory. That, however, is only one man's experience.

Winterizing a camera is something that should be done only by qualified camera repair men. *All* lubrication must be removed, the moving parts cleaned thoroughly, and the camera relubricated with silicone oils and greases.

If you take 10 more men, 5 will tell you that the silicone oils and greases are permanent for all climates and 5 will tell you it is best to have your cameras cleaned again on return from the ice, otherwise they will rust. In each case, it is best to ask the people who do the winterizing. It is true that late models of some of the expensive cameras have all-climate lubrication and need not be touched.

What happens to ordinary lubricants in the Antarctic is exactly what you would expect—they freeze. Most cameras won't work too well with their delicate moving parts encased in an oil the consistency of which is about that of chewing gum.

An alternative to silicone lubricants is the armpit. It is one I used, and, although it is a bit of a nuisance, it does work. You just keep the camera zipped inside your jacket until you're ready to shoot, take it out just long enough to take your shot, and then tuck it back inside. Tucked up into your armpit, a camera stays pretty warm.

CHOICE OF CAMERA

There is, of course, no all-inclusive advice for the selection of a camera. Whatever you like to shoot with, is the camera to use. For my own purpose, I took a Canon with Nikkor lenses and a single-lens reflex Yashica Pentamatic. Both served extremely well.

Loading is difficult and uncomfortable in exposed areas of ice, and I found that having two 35mm cameras with 72 exposures on hand was a blessing. My favorite Rollei stayed behind in New Zealand—12 shots just didn't seem enough, and a camera bigger than a 35mm is a bit bulky under the clothing. One rule seems to apply —the simpler the camera, the fewer the problems. Constant adjustments are a real source of annoyance. Cameras that use the film to cock the shutter are unsatisfactory—cold, brittle film will crack in these cameras.

The choice of camera would seem to depend (1) on your own preference and experience, (2) on the size negative you want to work with, (3) on the type of film best suited to your needs, and (4) on the need for interchangeable lenses. As any photographer will tell you, cameras are like wives and neckties, every man should choose his own.

FILM

In a word, film becomes brittle in the extreme cold, and extra care must be taken if priceless, one-time-only shots are not to be lost. If your camera has a rapid advance, use it sparingly. Advance your film in two or three easy stages, or (1) you may snap your brittle film or (2) get static electricity flashes because of the extreme dryness. The same rules apply, of course, when you rewind.

The choice of film is like the selection of a camera. Your own experience should be your guide, with this one word of advice—take more slow film than fast. Ice and snow are highly reflectant, and there is far more light than you need for high-ASA films. A film with an ASA rating of 50 can frequently be used at a speed of $\frac{1}{250}$ second at $f/11$ to $f/22$. One more word—take lots of color. The Antarctic is not a black-and-white place; it is a place of violent color extremes and lovely, subtle, gradations. Be careful in handling film in the extreme cold—the edges become very sharp and can give a nasty cut.

EXPOSURE

We have already pointed out that slow film is all you will probably ever need, night and day, for exteriors; but there are a few other points worth mentioning. Even if you are good enough to work without a light meter at home, don't try it on the ice. Light is extremely tricky in high-reflectance areas, and a meter is essential. Two meters are better than one when the nearest camera store is 2500 miles away.

It seems to be a strange contradiction to say that more people underexpose on the ice than overexpose, but it is true. The answer is simple and is psychological rather than photographic—overcompensation! *Use your meter!*

The advice given to me by a Navy photographer is extremely worth while—when in doubt, bracket your shot. If you get a reading of $f/11$ at $\frac{1}{250}$, shoot it that way and also at $f/8$ and $f/16$. Film is far cheaper than going back for a second try at a penguin marriage ceremony. I found, by my own experience, that I lost a great many more shots than I would have if I had bracketed.

CARE OF THE CAMERA

This rule applies to any very cold situation: when you bring your camera out of the cold into a heated room, put it on the floor, away from the source of heat, and forget it for at least an hour. After an hour, put it up on a box or something else, about a foot off the floor, and leave it for another hour. Later raise it some more for yet another hour. After the third or fourth hour and change in altitude, you can unload it. Both film and camera will have returned to normal slowly and, more important, moisture will not have condensed, as it would have from quick warming. If you do get condensation in your camera, you are in trouble. No sooner will you go out to shoot than your camera will freeze up like a cake of ice. You will have ice in your works and ice on the inside of your lens.

Photography in the Antarctic is thrilling, because you know you are taking pictures few other people have had an opportunity to focus in on. It is thrilling, too, because the pictures you are taking will have a greater meaning in the years ahead. People may not ask to see the pictures you took in New Orleans or Lake Placid, but they will ask to see the pictures you took of the South Pole. Photography in Antarctica is very rewarding but, like everything else at the bottom of the world, requires a special technique.

6

U.S. Antarctic Ships

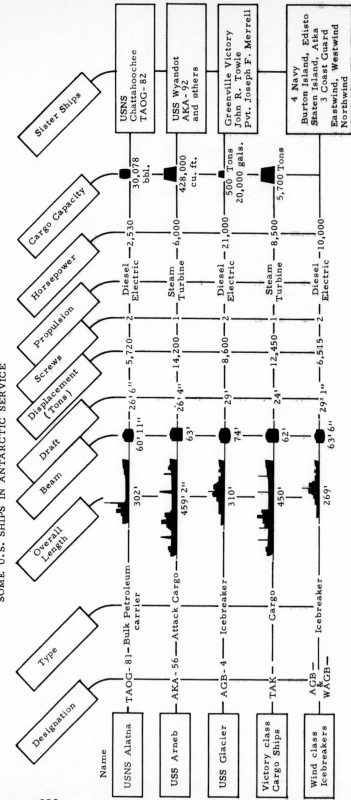

7

Antarctic Tracked Vehicles

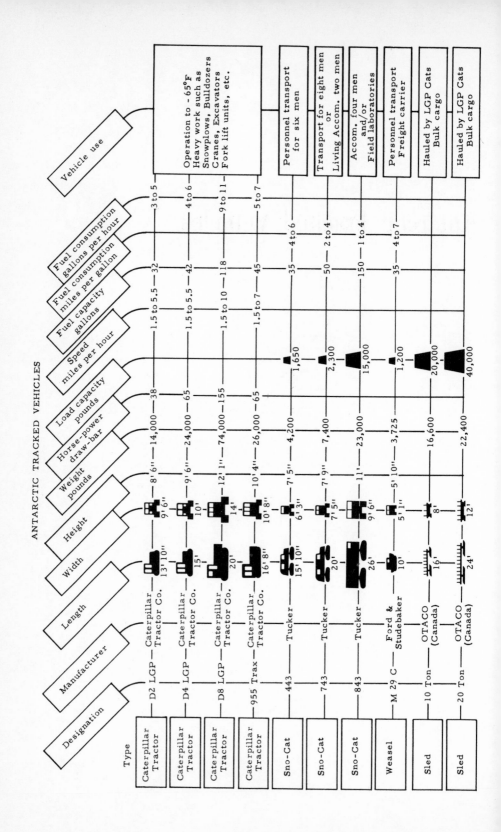

ANTARCTIC TRACKED VEHICLES

8

U.S. Antarctic Aircraft

U.S. ANTARCTIC AIRCRAFT

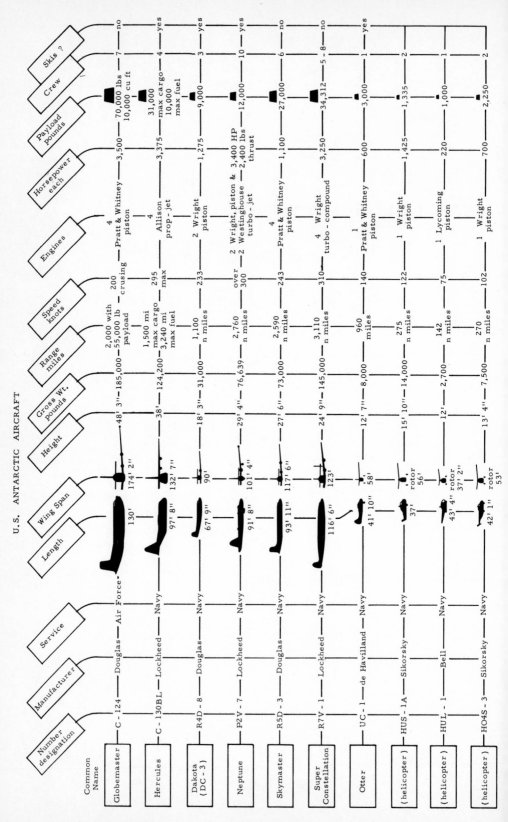

Common Name	Number designation	Manufacturer	Service	Length	Wing Span	Height	Gross Wt. pounds	Range miles	Speed knots	Engines	Horsepower each	Payload pounds	Crew	Skis?
Globemaster	C-124	Douglas	Air Force	130'	174' 2"	48' 3"	185,000	2,000 with 55,000 lb payload	200 crusing	4 Pratt & Whitney piston	3,500	70,000 lbs 10,000 cu ft	7	no
Hercules	C-130BL	Lockheed	Navy	97' 8"	132' 7"	38'	124,200	1,500 mi max cargo 3,240 mi max fuel	295 max	4 Allison prop-jet	3,375	31,000 max cargo 10,000 max fuel	4	yes
Dakota (DC-3)	R4D-8	Douglas	Navy	67' 9"	90'	18' 3"	31,000	1,100 n miles	233	2 Wright piston	1,275	9,000	3	yes
Neptune	P2V-7	Lockheed	Navy	91' 8"	101' 4"	29' 4"	76,639	2,760 n miles	over 300	2 Wright, piston & 2 Westinghouse turbo-jet	3,400 HP 2,400 lbs thrust	12,000	10	yes
Skymaster	R5D-3	Douglas	Navy	93' 11"	117' 6"	27' 6"	73,000	2,590 n miles	243	4 Pratt & Whitney piston	1,100	27,000	6	no
Super Constellation	R7V-1	Lockheed	Navy	116' 6"	123'	24' 9"	145,000	3,110 n miles	310	4 Wright turbo-compound	3,250	34,312	5 - 8	no
Otter	UC-1	de Havilland	Navy	41' 10"	58'	12' 7"	8,000	960 miles	140	1 Pratt & Whitney piston	600	3,000	1	yes
(helicopter)	HUS-1A	Sikorsky	Navy	37'	rotor 56'	15' 10"	14,000	275 n miles	122	1 Wright piston	1,425	1,335	2	
(helicopter)	HUL-1	Bell	Navy	43' 4"	rotor 37' 2"	12'	2,700	142 n miles	75	1 Lycoming piston	220	1,000	1	
(helicopter)	HO4S-3	Sikorsky	Navy	42' 1"	rotor 53'	13' 4"	7,500	270 n miles	102	1 Wright piston	700	2,250	2	

Abridged Bibliography

A COMPLETE Antarctic bibliography would fill several volumes. The quantity of written material that exists on any subject is a fair indication of man's curiosity about it, and, conversely, man's curiosity is a good indication of the amount that has been written. As we have pointed out, man has long been very curious about Antarctica.

The following extremely abbreviated list offers some titles that I have found particularly useful. Some volumes listed include the Antarctic, in with a lot of other material; and, going to the other extreme, some treat, very technically, one small aspect of the bottom of our world. Many books listed have bibliographies far exceeding this one in size. This list, however, is a good starting point. An hour or two in a library with this list will get you started. You yourself will soon determine how far you wish to go. May I wish you a very pleasant journey.

AMUNDSEN, ROALD E.: 1927, *My Life as an Explorer*, New York.

AUSTIN, OLIVER L., JR.: 1961, *Birds of the World*, Golden Press, New York.

BARNES, HOWARD T.: 1928, *Ice Engineering*, Renouf, Montreal, Canada.

BELL, CORYDON: 1957, *The Wonder of Snow*, Hill & Wang, New York.

BETTEX, ALBERT: 1960, *The Discovery of the World*, Simon & Schuster, New York

BRANDT, KARL: 1940, *Whale Oil—An Economic Analysis*, Food Research Institute, Stanford University, California.

BUDKER, PAUL: 1959, *Whales and Whaling*, Macmillan, New York.

BYRD, RICHARD E.: 1938, *Alone*, Putnam, New York.

CARRINGTON, RICHARD: 1960, *A Biography of the Sea*, Chatto & Windus, London.

COOK, CAPTAIN JAMES: *Journals* (1768–1779).

DAKIN, WILLIAM J.: 1934, *Whalemen Adventures*, Angus and Robertson, Sydney, Australia.

DALY, REGINALD A.: 1934, *The Changing World of the Ice Age*, Yale University Press, New Haven.

DEBENHAM, FRANK: 1960, *Discovery and Exploration,* Doubleday, New York.

FRAZIER, PAUL W.: 1959, *Antarctic Assault,* Dodd, Mead, New York.

FREUCHEN, PETER: 1957, *Book of the Seven Seas,* Julian Messner, New York.

FUCHS, VIVIAN (and Edmund Hillary): 1958, *The Crossing of Antarctica,* Little, Brown, Boston.

GREELY, ADOLPHUS W.: 1929, *The Polar Regions in the 20th Century,* Harrap, London.

HARDY, ALISTER C.: 1959, *The Open Sea,* 2 Vols., The New Naturalist, Collins, London.

HAYES, JAMES G.: 1932, *Conquest of the South Pole,* Butterworth, London.

HERALD, EARL S.: 1961, *Living Fishes of the World,* Doubleday, New York.

HERMANN, PAUL: 1958, *The Great Age of Discovery,* Harpers, New York.

LANSING, ALFRED: 1959, *Endurance,* McGraw-Hill, New York.

LEITHAUSER, JOACHIM G.: 1955, *Worlds Beyond the Horizon,* Knopf, New York.

MARKHAM, CLEMENTS R.: 1921, *The Lands of Silence,* University Press, Cambridge.

RONNE, FINN: 1961, *Antarctic Command,* Bobbs-Merrill, New York.

SANDERSON, IVAN T.: 1956, *Follow the Whale,* Little, Brown, Boston.

SCHEFFER, VICTOR B.: 1958, *Seals, Sea Lions and Walruses,* Stanford University Press, Stanford, California.

SCHULTHESS, EMIL: 1960, *Antarctica—A Photographic Survey,* Simon & Schuster, New York.

SCOTT, ROBERT F.: 1905, *The Voyage of The Discovery,* 2 Vols., Smith, Elder, London.

————: 1913, *Scott's Last Expedition,* 2 Vols., Smith, Elder, London.

SHACKLETON, ERNEST H.: 1909, *The Heart of the Antarctic,* 2 Vols., Lippincott, Philadelphia.

SULLIVAN, WALTER: 1957, *Quest for a Continent,* McGraw-Hill, New York.

————: 1961, *Assault on the Unknown,* McGraw-Hill, New York.

U.S. BOARD ON GEOGRAPHIC NAMES: 1956, *Geographic Names of Antarctica,* U.S. Government Printing Office, Washington, D.C.

Note: This list does not include references to periodic literature, for the quantity of this literature is absolutely overwhelming. Anyone seriously interested in any particular phase of Antarctic studies will find this source most rewarding and is referred to the various cumulative indices which most excellently do the task this small reference section could not hope to do.

Index

204

Mammals, 79-109 (*see also* Whales, Seals)
Mapping, 64, 152
Marble, 142
Marie, 8
Marie Byrd Land, *Fig. p. 134,* 138
Marine worms, 128
Martin Marietta Corp., 43, 137
Mask, 75
Mathiessen, Peter, 112
Mawson, Douglas, 27, 28, 36
McMurdo Sound, 20, 61, *Fig. p. 61,* 62, *Fig. p. 62,* 63, 120, 137, 138, 140
Medical equipment, 64-65
Megaptera böops (*nodosa*), 83
Mellors, Malcolm, 156
Men swallowed by whales, 87-88
Metabolism of seals, 101
Meteorite, 148
Meteorology, 65, 145
Mexico, 1
Mica, 142
Microscopic plants, 79, 128
Migration, seals, 107
Migration, whales, 81, 82, 87
Military, 40
Minerals, 43, 64, 141, 142, 155
Mining, 142
Mirny, 15, 17
Mirny Base, 15
Mirounga leonina, 97
Mites, 126-27
Mittens, 75
Moas, 111
Molybdenum, 142
Moraines, 53
Mosquito, 126, 155
Moss, 127
Moutonne, 58
Mystacoceti, 81

National Academy of Sciences, 95, 107, 131
National Research Council, 131
National Science Foundation, 37, 127, 156
Natural History magazine, 87
Névé, 56
New Byrd Station, 138
New Guinea, 111
New York Times, The, 107, 120
New Zealand, 2, 33, 61, 62, 63, 99, 107, 111, 112, 118, 158, 159
Nikkor lens, 192
Nimrod, 28
Nobile, Genl., 27
Non-militarization, 40
Norge, 27
North Pole, 6, 22, 27, 34
North Star, 35
Norway, 8, 9
Norwegian expeditions, 15, 19, 27
Notornis, 111

Nototheniidae, 129
Notothenoid fish, 129
Nuclear power, 43, 137, 138, 139, *Fig. p. 140, Fig. p. 143*
Nunataks, 53

Oases, 107, 142, 156
Oates, L., 24, 25
Ocean currents, 3, 144-45
Oceanography, 34, 141
Octopus, 43, 87, 128
Odontoceti, 81
Oil, 141-42
Ommatophoca rossi, 97
Operation Deep Freeze, 20, 36, 37, 42, 43
Operation High Jump, 35
Orcinus orca, 88
Ostrich, 110-11
Otter, 8
Ozone, 145, 147

Pack ice, 14, 20, 30, 31, 58
Pagodroma nivea, 123
Palmer, Nat. B., 16, 17, 43
Palmer Peninsula, 11, 16, 30, 127, 155
Parachute, 66
Patagonia, 131
Peary, Adm. R., 22
Pebbles, 118-120
Pelecypods, 82
Pelicans, 112
Pendleton, Benjamin, 16
Penguins, 14, 89, 92, 94, 103, 106, 110-115, 122, 125, 155
    Adelie, 112, *Fig. p. 114,* 118, 119, 120, *Fig. p. 121,* 122
    Emperor, 103, 112, *Figs. pp. 113, 115, 116, 117, 119,* 119, 120, 122
Penney, Richard L., 120
Permanent ice, 47
Permian period, 1
Perspiration, 73
Peter Snow Miller, *Fig. p. 137*
Petrels, 116, 123
Pezophaps, 111
Philately, 188-190
Phosphorous, 142
Photography, 65, 191-194
Physeter catodon, 87
Piedmont glacier, 57
Pilot whale, 81, 87
Pinguinis, 111
Pinks, 127
Pinnipedia (*see* Seals)
Piri Reis, 10, 11, 178
Place names, 176-77
Plankton, 79, 81, 82, 138
Plant life, 1, 4, 79, 127, 132, 158
Plasticity of ice, 49, 50, 67
Plasticity of the earth, 148, 155, 157, 158
Plantanistids, 81
Plunder fish, 129

ROGER A. CARAS

34-year-old author of Antarctica: Land of Frozen Time, *thinks of himself as two people. On the one hand, he is a busy young executive with Columbia Pictures Corporation, carrying an attaché case and wearing "the right tie with the right suit," while on the other, he is a kind of intellectual prospector with a battered wardrobe and perennial enthusiasm.*

His chief "outside interest" is the world, and he is dedicated to the two tasks of seeing it all and understanding as much of it as he can. A member of the famed Explorers Club of New York, he has crossed the Pacific 12 times and the Atlantic twice. He has spent time in 43 of the 50 states and "looked under rocks" in some "pretty strange places." He is an amateur naturalist, anthropologist, and beachcomber, and a semi-professional photographer.

Mr. Caras lives with his wife, son, daughter, and his "private zoo" and collections in the Kew Gardens section of New York City.